IDENTITY AND ART THERAPY

52

IDENTITY AND ART THERAPY

Personal and Professional Perspectives

MAXINE BOROWSKY JUNGE

(With 22 Other Art Therapists Contributors)

CHARLES C THOMAS • PUBLISHER, LTD.
Springfield • Illinois • U.S.A.

Published and Distributed Throughout the World by

CHARLES C THOMAS • PUBLISHER, LTD.
2600 South First Street
Springfield, Illinois 62704

© 2014 by CHARLES C THOMAS • PUBLISHER, LTD.

ISBN 978-0-398-08796-8 (paper)
ISBN 978-0-398-08797-5 (ebook)

Library of Congress Catalog Card Number: 2013049067

With THOMAS BOOKS *careful attention is given to all details of manufacturing
and design. It is the Publisher's desire to present books that are satisfactory as to their
physical qualities and artistic possibilities and appropriate for their particular use.*
THOMAS BOOKS *will be true to those laws of quality that assure a good name
and good will.*

*Printed in the United States of America
MM-R-3*

Library of Congress Cataloging-in-Publication Data

Identity and art therapy : personal and professional perspectives /
edited by Maxine Borowsky June ; with 22 other art therapists
contributors.
        pages cm
    Includes bibliographical references.
    ISBN 978-0-398-08796-8 (pbk.) -- ISBN 978-0-398-08797-5 (ebook)
    1. Art therapy. 2. Psychotherapy–Practice–Psychological aspects.
3. Psychotherapist and patient. 4. Identity (Psychology). I. Junge,
Maxine Borowsky, editor of compilation.

RC489.A7.126 2014
616.89′1656–dc23
                                        2013049067

CONTRIBUTORS

Pat B. Allen, PhD, ATR, HLM, is an author, artist, and art therapist. Her books–*Art Is a Way of Knowing* (Shambhala, 1995) and *Art Is a Spiritual Path* (Shambhala, 2005)-explore the borders between art, psychology, spirituality, and social action. She lives in Ojai, California, exploring her passion for the landscape.

Charlotte Boston, MA, ATR-BC, has provided art therapy services for more than 28 years in the mid-Atlantic region of the United States. Her experiences include clinical work with various populations and age levels of inpatient military and residential patients with a broad range of diagnoses. She has served as Director of Expressive Therapy and Clinical Director in inpatient settings. She has been an art therapy supervisor, consultant, and lecturer and is currently Adjunct Professor at the George Washington University Art Therapy master's program.

Sarah Deaver, PhD, ATR-BC, has been an art therapy educator, researcher, and clinician over 25 years. A professor at the Eastern Virginia Medical School (EVMS), her scholarly interests include art therapy educational theory and practice as well as art therapy and efficacy research. At EVMS she is the Research Director of the Graduate Art Therapy and Counseling Program, teaches the program's research curriculum and ethics course, and provides clinical supervision to students. She has presented prolifically and has published numerous articles and book chapters. She is the incoming president of the American Art Therapy Association.

Elizabeth Donahue, MA, ATR, LMHC, joined the Antioch University–Seattle faculty as an Adjunct in 2010 and is now full-time teaching faculty. She has worked as an art therapist in a community mental health setting and a residential treatment facility for adolescents and maintains a private practice in Seattle, where she specializes in the treatment of children and adolescents who are experiencing symptoms related to depression, anxiety, and trauma.

Nancy Gerber, PhD, ATR-BC, LPC, is Clinical Associate Professor and Director of the Doctorate in Creative Arts Therapies and former Director of the master's degree in Art Therapy at Drexel University in Philadelphia. She has presented and published on art therapy assessment, doctoral education for art therapists, mixed methods research, and art-based research. Dr. Gerber was the first recipient of the Distinguished Educator's Award from the American Art Therapy Association.

David Gussak, PhD, ATR-BC, is Chair of the Department of Art Education and Clinical Coordinator of the Graduate Art Therapy Program for Florida State University in Tallahassee. He has published and presented extensively on art therapy in correctional settings and with violent and aggressive clients. His latest book, *Art on Trial: Art Therapy in Capital Murder Cases,* is available from Columbia University Press. With Marcia Rosal, he is currently at work on *The Wiley-Blackwell Handbook of Art Therapy.*

Janice Hoshino, PhD, ATR-BC, LMHC, is Chair of Art and Drama Therapies Programs and faculty member in the Marriage and Family Therapy Program at Antioch University, Seattle. She received her doctorate from U.S. International University (now Alliant) in San Diego. She has previously taught art therapy at Marywood College in Scranton, PA, and Emporia State University in Kansas and is a board member of the Art Therapy Certification Board (ATCB.) Her publications include *Family Art Therapy* (co-author) and the "People of Color in Art Therapy" series (co-author) in *Art Therapy, Journal of the American Art Therapy Association.* Her primary focus is multiculturalism, and she received the Pearlie Robison Award from the American Art Therapy Association for her work in multiculturalism.

Don Jones, ATR-BC, HLM, is a full-time artist-clinician, painter and sculptor, and founder and past President and Honorary Life Member of the American Art Therapy Association and the Buckeye Art Therapy Association. He worked six years at the Menninger Clinic in Topeka, Kansas, and retired from Harding Hospital in Ohio after 22 years. In retirement, he continues with private studio practice, workshops, mentoring, lecturing, consulting, and working artfully with those wanting to be "weller-than-well."

Karen Rush Jones, MA, ATR-BC, is an art therapist and artist of more than 35 years. She has worked in psychiatry, teaching, and, most recently, bereavement services with HomeReach Hospice in Columbus, Ohio. She says, "Making art is a way of attending to one's own life. The interior landscape is as real and important as that of the exterior world." Jones is co-author with Don Jones of the essay in this book, "Why Art Therapists Must Make Art."

Frances F. Kaplan, MPS, DA, ATR-BC, holds a doctorate in art therapy from New York University. She has extensive experience teaching, practicing, publishing and presenting in the field and is the author of *Art, Science and Art Therapy,* and *Art Therapy and Social Action.* She is currently at work on a book about art therapy assessments. Dr. Kaplan was the Executive Editor of *Art Therapy, Journal of the American Art Therapy Association.* A past director of the art therapy Master's program at Hofstra University, she has taught at Marylhurst University in Oregon since 1997.

Myra Levick, PhD, ATR-BC, HLM, established the creative arts therapy program at Hahnemann Hospital and Medical College (now Drexel University) in Philadelphia, the first graduate art therapy program in the United States. She is one of the founders of the American Art Therapy Association and its first president (1969–1971). She was editor of *The Arts in Psychotherapy: An International Journal* and has published many books and articles. Dr. Levick's books center around children's art and their developmental processes. Some are *They Could Not Talk and So They Drew: Children's Styles of Coping and Thinking* and *See What I'm Saying: What Children Tell Us Through Their Drawings.* Her 2009 publication is the *Levick Emotional and Cognitive Art Therapy Assessment: A Normative Study.* She lives in Florida.

Debra Linesch, PhD, MFT, ATR-BC, is Chair and Director of the Graduate Program in Marital and Family Therapy, Specializing in Clinical Art Therapy at Loyola Marymount University (LMU). She is the author of many articles and five books, including *Adolescent Art Therapy, Art Therapy With Families in Crisis, Celebrating Family Milestones Through Art Making, Facing Genesis: Visual Midrash, and Midrashic Mirrors: Creating Holiness in Imagery and Intimacy.* She developed LMU's Art Therapy in Mexico collaboration with Universidad Iberoamericana, an intercultural training, research, and service endeavor, and she is currently establishing a research institute in the department.

Cathy Malchiodi, PhD, LPCC, LPAT, ATR-BC, HLM, is the President of Art Therapy Without Borders and Director of the Trauma-informed Practices and Expressive Arts Therapy Institute. She has written and/or edited 18 books including *The Art Therapy Sourcebook, Handbook of Art Therapy, Art Therapy and Health Care,* and *Understanding Children's Drawings.* Dr. Malchiodi has given more than 350 invited keynote addresses, workshops, and courses throughout the United States and internationally. She is an Honorary Life Member of the American Art Therapy Association and received Kennedy Center Honors for her international work in art therapy. She is also a syndicated writer for *Psychology Today* and gave the very first TEDX talk on art therapy in October 2012.

Mercedes ter Maat, PhD, LPC, ATR-BC, is the current President of the American Art Therapy Association. She is an art therapist and Associate Professor of Counselor Education in the graduate programs at Nova Southeastern University in Fort Lauderdale, Florida. Dr. ter Maat practices, teaches and conducts research in the areas of ethics, multicultural counseling and risk, and protective factors of cultural minority families and youth.

Brenda Maltz, BA, RN, CCM, is working on graduate studies and mental health counseling at Antioch University, Seattle. She is transitioning to the field after more than 30 years as a nurse and case manager specializing in the care of trauma patients and adults with chronic illnesses. She is a sculptor with bronze pieces in private and public collections across the United States.

Kim Newall, BFA, is currently pursuing her graduate degree in art therapy and mental health counseling at Antioch University, Seattle. She is an artist-in-residence and educational consultant in the arts throughout Washington state, working with children and adults in educational settings. Her passion for psychology, creativity, and spirituality has finally found a synthesis in the field of art therapy.

Jordan Potash, PhD, ATR-BC, REAT, LCAT, is faculty, consultant and Expressive Art Therapy Program Coordinator at the Centre on Behavioral Health, University of Hong Kong. He is primarily interested in the applications of art and art therapy in the service of community development and social change, with an emphasis on reducing stigma, confronting discrimination, and promoting cross-cultural relationships.

Arthur Robbins, EDD, ATR, HLM, was Professor of Creative Art Therapy at Pratt Institute in New York City and was a founder of the program. He is also the founding director for the Institute for Expressive Analysis. He is a licensed psychologist and psychoanalyst as well as a sculptor. His books include *Creative Art Therapy, The Artist as Therapist,* and *The Psychoaesthetic Experience.* Dr. Robbins' memoir appears in Junge & Wadeson's book, *Architects of Art Therapy, Memoirs and Life Stories.*

Marcia L. Rosal, PhD, ATR-BC, HLM, is Professor and Director of the Florida State University Art Therapy Program. She is a past president of the American Art Therapy Association (AATA). Throughout her career, she has chaired numerous AATA committees and continues to serve on the Conference Program, Honors, and Research Committees. She was the Founding Senior Editor for the *Journal of Art for Life* (2009–2012) and is on the editorial boards of *The Journal of Art for Life, Clinical Art Therapy* and *The Arts in Psychotherapy.* She has lectured nationally and internationally and is a Fullbright Scholar. Over the years, she has published numerous articles and chapters on art therapy. With David Gussak, Rosal is currently at work on *The Wiley-Blackwell Handbook of Art Therapy.*

Judith A. Rubin, PhD, ATR-BC, HLM, is past President and Honorary Life Member of the American Art Therapy Association. She is Professor Emerita at the Pittsburgh Psychoanalytic Institute and a faculty member at the University of Pittsburgh. She is the author of six books and ten films about art therapy and is President of Expressive Media, Inc. (http://www .espressivemedia.org). Two of her books are *Child Art Therapy, Art Therapy: An Introduction* and *Approaches to Art Therapy.*

Gwendolyn McPhaul Short, MA, ATR-BC, lives in Washington D.C., and received her degree from George Washington University. Since 1976 she has served on many committees of the American Art Therapy Association and assisted with the creation of the film, "Wheels of Diversity: Pioneers of Color in Art Therapy." Her memoir appeared in the "People of Color" series in *Art Therapy, Journal of the American Art Therapy Assocation.*

Harriet Wadeson, PhD, LCSW, ATR-BC, HLM, has directed art therapy programs at the University of Houston, the University of Illinois, and Northwestern University, over a period of 35 years. She has published eight books on art therapy, approximately 70 papers, and numerous chapters in psychology and art therapy texts. She is a frequently invited national keynote speaker and an international guest lecturer in 14 countries and has led professional delegations to many of them. Dr. Wadeson has received awards for her artwork, her educational contributions and her research, including a first prize from the Smithsonian Institute for art, a Distinguished Faculty Award from Northwestern University, the Benjamin Rush Award from the American Psychiatric Association, and a Resolution of Commendation from the Illinois Legislature.

For Benjamin,
With love

Works by Maxine Borowsky Junge

A History of Art Therapy in the United States
(With Paige Asawa)

Creative Realities, the Search for Meanings

Architects of Art Therapy, Memoirs and Life Stories
(With Harriet Wadeson)

Mourning, Memory and Life Itself, Essays by an Art Therapist

The Modern History of Art Therapy in the United States

Graphic Facilitation and Art Therapy,
Imagery and Metaphor in Organizational Development
(With Michelle Winkle)

Identity and the Art Therapist

PREFACE

Nearly every morning I walk with my dog Betsy through the woods near the Margurite Bron Dog Park on Whidbey Island in Washington where I live. Some years ago, I walked on the headlands of Mendocino, California, with the ends of the coastal land–the rocky bluffs–open to the crash of the ocean; constant attention needed to be paid to stay firmly on the uneven path. Unlike Mendocino's expansiveness, in the woods where I walk now, tall evergreens of the Pacific Northwest woods form a protective and silent cozy cradle where only flashes of light come in and where I can dream. With fall winds, Betsy wears her red and black checked coat, and evergreen needles come down to form a brown carpet on the path. I watch leaves dry up, turn yellow, and float from the Bigleaf Maples, and I hear my footfalls crunching. In winter, rains appear and sometimes ice and snow, and then, always a surprise and as if by magic, spring green flows as the leaves fluff out the trees and make them dense again. On those daily walks, I fantasize, construct, and, ultimately, write my books. Of course, when I get to the computer, the words and phrases are nowhere near as striking as those I find in the woods. I once concocted a theory that if one goes outside on a wet foggy night, all the lost bits from computers can be seen hanging in the trees.

Identity, the subject of this book, can be a huge muddle; it is nowhere near as neat or coherent as it is usually thought to be nor is it as opaque as the leaves in the woods. Depending on perspective, identity can and does vary by context. Transparent, it shifts constantly, is always malleable, and is intensely fluid–full of contradictions, tensions, and paradoxes existing together, often making little logical sense. Still we talk and write of identity as an "object" as if we could capture it and pin it to a board to study.

I have been thinking about art therapy identity and its development for many years–before I became an art therapist and certainly since. With the variety of books I have written with their vastly different foci, it must appear to some that I'm harboring a diagnosis of Attention Deficit Disorder. But visible or not, there is an overarching meta theme flowing through all: Implicitly, my books are about identity–my own and art therapy's–and about how the field of American art therapy positions itself on art, psychology, clinical practice, and education.

Although seldom formally discussed, throughout my career, most of my writing has been an attempt to describe and proclaim art therapy's identity. *The Modern History of Art Therapy* (2010) and before it *A History of Art Therapy in the United States* (1994) are examples, in that a profession must have a coherent, contextualized, and preferably *written* history and identity to move forward—and American art therapy does.

It is my suspicion that art therapists consciously and unconsciously think about identity as they go about their day-to-day business; its shifts, twists, and turns have provided a basic truth for the field. Identity has been vociferously argued forever, openly and behind the scenes in organized art therapy, overtly and directly and in unconscious, subliminal language. This book is my attempt to afford art therapy identity the out-front and clear position it deserves. Despite my efforts toward clarity, there will nevertheless remain here many contradictory notions, often paradoxically existing at the same time. That is the nature of identity and of art therapy's identity.

I remember a panel at a long-ago American Art Therapy Conference, which asked, "If you were awakened in the middle of the night and asked the question, 'Are you an artist or a therapist?' what would you answer?" Panelist Robert Ault replied, "An artist!" The question implies that there are only two correct answers and that art therapists may innately be more one than the other. I reject this idea and propose that "art therapy" is neither a form of artist nor a form of therapist, but rather a *whole new field*—a separate and special profession with core values and attributes of its own that must lead to a special and separate identity.

Chapter 1 is the "Introduction" to this book. In Chapter 2, "Images of Identity," I lay a basic groundwork describing definitions of personal and professional identity and discuss the concept of "intersectionality." Then the history and evolution of identity in the field of American art therapy are described. Finally, I argue for art therapy as a new profession that is not simply an offshoot of either art or therapy.

Living and surviving in the real world is a particularly tricky pathway for art therapists with hazards suddenly appearing out of the darkness, like skeletons in a carnival ride. Chapter 3, "Living in the Real World," discusses some unique problems faced by art therapists as they strive to achieve personal and professional identity and credibility. In Chapter 3, I describe challenges that art therapy currently encounters and, in particular, discuss dual-degree educational training programs and what they may mean to identity.

Chapter 4, "Essays on Identity by Art Therapists," contains twenty-one essays by prominent art therapists who were invited to contribute their ideas.

A prelude to this chapter is a list of Contributors. These essays can be considered different "readings" of what identity is in the art therapy field. I invited people with different ideas and from different "generations" to participate. As it turned out, most of the art therapists who wrote essays have been in the field for a number of years and are intimately acquainted with the field's evolution. Two contributors are students. I said that honesty and a willingness to express one's opinions were crucial. I wrote, "This is your opportunity to say some of those things you may have been thinking for a long time" (Appendix A is "Letter to Potential Book Contributors"). To art therapists who agreed to participate, I sent "Fifteen Defining Questions," which I invited them to use in their essays or not (these questions appear as Appendix B). The essay chapter concludes with a "Summary" outlining characteristics of the group of writers and illuminating major repetitive themes.

Chapter 5, "Identity Initiative, Steps Toward a New Definition: An Action Plan," describes a two-year process, including all segments of the art therapy community to achieve and promulgate a shared public professional identity. Chapter 6 underscores "Conclusions."

Curious to discover some baseline information about identity for students entering graduate art therapy programs, I constructed a brief questionnaire and contacted three art therapy master's program directors who agreed to conduct my survey with their entering students in fall, 2012. In addition, I searched out a few recent graduates to get some ideas about the nature of their identity when people finished their graduate programs and began their careers. These mini-surveys were not formal, scientific research studies and should not be considered as such, nor were they intended to evaluate the programs concerned. I merely hoped to generate some ideas about identity from these specific populations of art therapy students and graduates.

While I have tried to be fair and objective, the ideas in this book (except for the essays) are obviously my own, and I assume there will be some, perhaps many, who will disagree and want to argue. In large part, an important and essential discussion of the nuances of identity by the art therapy community is a significant intention of this book.

Identity and Art Therapy is primarily written for art therapists—experienced ones and novices. It is for those who teach them now and for people thinking about entering the field in the future. In addition, this book has a frankly acknowledged social action goal: By bringing into the light and illuminating concepts of personal and professional identity in American art therapy as it has been and is now, I hope to clearly show that identity *IS a core issue for art therapy,* which needs careful reexamination and definition for the 21st century.

I am fascinated with the development and history of the healing professions in general, and I suspect that they have similar and perhaps even universal evolutionary stages. *Identity and Art Therapy* may be of interest to mental health professionals of all stripes who can find reflections of their own struggles in this story. Implicit, but not directly spoken of, in much of the clinical writing by art therapists is some sense of personal and professional identity. Nonetheless, this is the first book to explicitly focus on issues of identity and to ask art therapists to publically give voice and presence to their ideas.

During its history, American art therapy has grown up and come of age. In this book, I have asked art therapists to think and write carefully about their own identity and that of the profession and to make suggestions for moving forward. I have tried to do that myself. The last chapters of the book then will be a suggested series of action steps to be taken by the art therapy community, educational programs, and the professional organizations, which I believe could help art therapy continue to survive and effectively grow.

ACKNOWLEDGMENTS

I am most grateful to all the art therapists who recognized that identity is an essential issue and took the time to write an essay for this book, when they had many other things to do. Their thoughtful words reflect a variety of viewpoints, and many contain fine suggestions for change.

Over my writing time, I have discussed many of the ideas in this book. I thank all those who were so willing to informally dialogue with me about the issues, over lunch, over drinks, around the fireplace, and driving in the car. My "Uninstructed Drawing Group" gets a loud clap for being ever provocative, useful, and pleasurable.

In particular, I thank Dr. Sarah Deaver of Eastern Virginia Medical Center for her help and knowledge of research in art therapy; Dr. Donna Kaiser, Director of Art Therapy Programs at Drexel University; and the directors of art therapy graduate programs who gave my questionnaires to their beginning students and new graduates. This population added data and insights and has my appreciation.

Scott and Jason of Lincoln Computers on Whidbey Island have kept me rolling technologically, and Chris Dennis took the pictures of my drawings for the cover and for the "About the Author" section.

My son, Benjamin Junge, Associate Professor of Anthropology at SUNY, to whom this book is dedicated, deserves more than my thanks. His steadiness, willingness to listen to my ideas and add his own, deep knowledge, and thoughtfulness have made this a much better book. In addition, he is my first line computer expert–always patient. And he doesn't try to teach me how to do it–he simply tells me how, so I can go on.

Michael Thomas of Charles C Thomas Publishers has published all but two of my books. He is the perfect publisher for me–supportive, helpful, and non-intrusive. I appreciate his humanity and that of his staff. His consistent publication of books over the years in and about art therapy must be mentioned as a major contribution to the identity of the profession.

I want to single out Trevor Ollech of Charles C Thomas, who has created the exceptional cover designs for my books. His work embodies creativity, uniqueness, and collaboration. I have been very lucky with his contributions, which I believe make an immense contribution to my work.

It is perhaps atypical to mention those people in one's life who helped through some very dark times, but there were many during the writing of this book. I expect they know who they are. I certainly hope so.

CONTENTS

IDENTITY AND ART THERAPY

The mind that has conceived a plan of living
must never lose sight of the chaos against
which that pattern was conceived.
–Ralph Ellison, *Invisible Man*

Chapter 1

INTRODUCTION

In this book I explore the crucial issue of art therapy identity. In preliminary chapters, I lay out definitions and challenges of the field as it attempts to continue to establish its credibility, values, and uniqueness. The next portion of the book is 21 essays—readings on identity by art therapists. Here the reader will find many differences, some confusion, and a little agreement. This is exactly the point of the book: I want to open a dialogue about what I believe is a seldom discussed and yet extraordinarily important issue. In the final chapters of the book, I outline a potential Action Plan for the art therapy community to take art therapy forward into what I hope will be an invigorating and exciting future.

Poet T.S. Eliot wrote about the end being the beginning. The end, he said, is where we start from, and as we explore, we return again to the beginning where we can really know it for the first time. My intention in this book is to shine a strong light on art therapy identity, in both its personal and professional vicissitudes at this unique historical time—the beginning decades of the 21st century. Looking back to see where we have been may enable us to go forward with more clarity and effectiveness. While what emerges may not all be pretty images, I believe it is a central necessity to understand what identity has been for art therapists individually and collectively and to recognize art therapy identity in its history as it ebbed and flowed and sometimes seemed a confusing and wrongheaded muddle. As William Faulker (2011) wrote in *Requium for a Nun,* "The past is never dead. It's not even past." We need to understand the polarization and competitiveness that initially apparently gripped the field and, some would say, still exists today. Finally, envisioning the leadership role that art therapy's most visible professional organization, the American Art Therapy Association (AATA), has played and continues to play today can lend clarity to what must be essential strategies for the profession of art therapy.

A slippery and confusing concept, individual identity often exists in considerable tension with concepts of group identity. Art therapy as a community has had a stunning history, in large measure built on its special core values of creativity in therapy. In many ways, it is amazing that art therapy has done as well as it has. But perhaps we have come now to be victims of some of our own success. While art therapy remains a relatively small profession, and probably always will, it holds within its reach and ambitions similarities to other evolving mental health professions, and, therefore, a reasoned inquiry is doubly important.

In the last 40 years or so, educational programs have trained and graduated art therapists across America. Typically, they emerge from the protective cocoon of graduate school into the reality of a highly competitive world of work and into a nation where the mental health system is financially unsupported, crumbling, and in dire straits–and it has been for a long time. Art therapists, like other students, often graduate with large loan debts that can impact their lives negatively for years to come.

I was an art therapist before I knew the words and before there was an established field of art therapy. Passionately interested in art since early childhood, I was always making art, trying to understand it and how it affected others. I grew up in Los Angeles during the McCarthy and Blacklist era. My father was a movie writer and professor of screenwriting and playwriting at UCLA. My mother had been a costume and scenic designer in New York Theater during the W.P.A./Depression era who became deaf in Los Angeles. Both my parents were painters.

My mother and father regularly had parties where conversation was central. In this innovative and flourishing world, writers and other Hollywood intellectuals, along with historians and psychoanalysts, talked ideas and politics. I remember the living room of our house on Forrester Drive where these gatherings took place. I remember sitting on the slip-covered yellow, orange, and blue couches that my mother had bought at Goodwill listening to the fascinating talk going on. From an early age, I was allowed to sit in. Listening quietly, I learned from the best. Sitting in, but seldom speaking (I was a child, after all), I picked up huge amounts of cultural information and learned how to effectively express ideas, take apart and tease out concept's meanings, argue, and, perhaps most importantly, to hear and understand the subtext underneath the obvious. These listening and subtext skills served me well when later I became an art psychotherapist. Perhaps I also realized my identity then as an outsider. From my parents, I learned a model of social justice, courage, and action during the McCarthy and Blacklist years, which engulfed the movie business and large portions of the United States.

I formally entered the art therapy field in 1973 and began teaching in Helen Landgarten's master's program at Immaculate Heart College in Hollywood, California-the first art therapy educational program in the West. Helen invented the term "clinical art therapist." By this, she meant an art therapist who was not necessarily a member of an inpatient psychiatric treatment team, but one who could carry the whole responsibility of the case, was "equal" in training to other mental health professionals, and who could function in outpatient psychiatric clinics.

In those days, before most people had any idea of what art therapy was or could be, Helen and I evolved a strategy for making art therapy known within the region by creating jobs for graduates; we considered it the crucial first priority, and, as good as our art therapy education was, we believed if a graduate couldn't get a job, it didn't matter. For us, excellent education was always tied to employment and awareness and expansion of the field. Sadly, many art therapy programs, historically and currently, do not integrate education and employment together in this way.

Helen and I reasoned that the way to expand knowledge and awareness of art therapy was to train the best clinicians we could and provide internships for them in local mental health clinics. We would show off the quality of art therapy through the superb students we trained. Many graduates were later employed by their internship sites or in other facilities. Once an art therapy "slot" was established at a clinic, we made sure it was passed on and continued.

Previously, Helen and Frances Anderson had carried out a series of studies concerning knowledge of the art therapy field. They sent a survey to mental health clinics asking, among other things, whether they would like an art therapy intern (Anderson , 1973; Anderson & Landgarten, 1974, 1975). Landgarten (1976, 1978) also sent the survey to clinics in the greater Los Angeles region. These questionnaires contained an inherent *public relations function,* in that they made the field more visible to clinics and clinicians who received and completed the survey and often created an agreement to provide an internship (free to the clinic) for an art therapist.

As mental health clinic staffs came in contact with art therapy interns and through them with art therapy, they learned about the innovative field and, Helen and I hoped, would become intrigued enough to make art therapy part of their clinic. This strategy usually worked, and many art therapists found employment as knowledge of and respect for the field expanded.

In the early days, very few art therapists were employed in clinics and mental health facilities in the Los Angeles area, so we asked that a state licensed staff member of the institution supervise[1] our interns while the program agreed to provide outside art therapy supervision. Over an academic year, the clinic staff member met weekly with the art therapy intern and saw the process of art therapy unfolding up close. They came to understand and appreciate art therapy and the art therapy intern. Born out of scarcity and necessity, this supervisory arrangement turned out to be a political gold mine because we had developed a respected clinic staff member "within" who could sing the praises of art therapy from personal experience.

Years later when the field's reach was much extended, many mental health clinicians had come pleasantly in contact with art therapy, and many art therapists had found employment, the master's program, now at Loyola Marymount University in Los Angeles, no longer needed clinic staff members to supervise because there were plenty of art therapists employed. However, we decided to continue this procedure because it had proven to be such an important *political strategy.* Helen was always cognizant about art therapy identity, and she taught me well:

---

1. A "supervisor" for a mental health trainee is the primary internship teacher and mentor. Intern and supervisor meet weekly for about an hour; the student goes over current cases and the artwork, and the supervisor helps the intern plan for the next client meetings. In this way, the inexperienced student has the advantage of the support and knowledge of an experienced clinician, and the client has the advantage of an experienced clinical mind involved in their treatment. Supervision also embodies a unique role model function. Currently, because of economic and time constraints, supervision may not be what it once was, but it is the central learning relationship in the novice therapist's process toward maturity and also can help avoid the problem of early burnout.

We were conscious of what we did and in everything tried to enhance and extend awareness of the field, its credibility, and its identity.

The major evolution of the art therapy field in the United States initially occurred during a time of economic expansion and an unsurpassed post-World War II necessity for creative expansions and interventions in mental health. In 1954, the development of a new variety of major tranquilizers made possible the release of many patients from psychiatric hospitals into the community. Through states, the Kennedy Community Mental Health Bill of 1963 poured money into outpatient community programs to aid the mentally impaired and provide services for those no longer in inpatient care. Art therapy was a beneficiary of this vision. The renewed national context for innovative mental health gave art therapy a running start and helped propel it forward. Unfortunately, times and the economic climate have changed.

The American Art Therapy Association (AATA), the first national professional organization for art therapy, was formed in 1969—45 years ago—giving art therapists from all over the United States a forum for dialogue and argument. A yearly conference brought art therapists together from disparate parts of the country, Canada, and, in later years, internationally. In 1970, Standards of Practice were established, leading to an art therapist registration process (ATR). Much later, "Board Certification" through an exam came into being. Guidelines for art therapy education programs were established in 1973 to begin laying out expectations for something of a standardized curriculum. In 1975, an accreditation-like procedure of "Approval" by the AATA arrived for art therapy educational programs meeting its standards.

It is no surprise to anyone that for the past years, we have endured a shrinking economy with a catastrophic unemployment rate and a foreclosed housing market. Millions are out of work and have lost their retirement plans. The "American Dream"—of working to support a family, acquiring a house, and then retiring—if not dead already is lingering close to death. While the economy may be turning around, life will undoubtedly look different in the future. It already does. Life expectancy has increased, and as the national population ages, cities, states, and economies struggle to stay alive. Many services that Americans saw as their right are devastated. Jobs and salaries for police, firemen, and teachers are cut to the bone, with the contemporary public encountering a different culture from what they have been used to and had come to expect. More mentally ill are homeless and on the streets or in jail; more mentally ill are in prisons untreated. What this means for professional mental health disciplines is that an already wounded and disrespected mental health system is suffering layoffs and cutbacks of essential services and is in real danger of disappearing entirely. Despite need, because of economic necessity and finances, treatment interventions have become almost wholly short term and behavioral. Societal violence is ubiquitous, with murders and even mass murders an almost daily reality. What this means for the art therapy profession is shrinking employment opportunities with the pragmatics of state licensing coming to the forefront.

Art therapy is based on the duality of art and psychology, and it has taken on increased duality in its theoretical base, as will be discussed more fully later. An analogy is the "nature/nurture" argument of human development: as genes have become better understood and genetics shown to be such an important part of the human being, in the last 40 years or so, the nature/nurture pendulum has swung to the "nature" spot, even though most with any common sense know that it is neither one nor the other but the *combination* of both that makes the difference. Today, a pill is thought by many to be a better and quicker option for solving complex mental health issues than the variety of longer therapies that were never effective at proving their value as a healing tool.

The practice of art therapy originally developed within Freudian psychodynamically based therapies counting on a progression of imagery over time. I speculate that the pendulum shift is one of the reasons for the current art therapy focus on the innate usefulness of the creative process and art therapy's movement into the community. The psychiatric environment has shrunk, has changed, and is close to disappearing. Like other mental health disciplines, art therapy is caught in this web and struggles to adapt.

We are a pill-addled society attempting to solve our problems with prescribed medications for those who can afford them. What this means for art therapy is that the expansive and creative times of the past are gone, and the surfeit of mental health workers educated in past years floods the market, making mere survival and the ability to achieve any living wage major issues. In today's climate, art therapy programs may educate many more students than can actually work as art therapists after they graduate.

Some years ago in Los Angeles, I met a man at a Board of Behavior Sciences meeting (the California State board regulating psychotherapy licensing). He told me he directed a Marriage and Family Therapy program at a local university, and he said it graduated 250 people a year. My mouth hung open, and I asked, "How do they get jobs?" I'll never forget his answer: "The cream rises to the top." Even the "cream" can't find employment anymore. Art therapy master's education has become an industry all its own, but as student clinicians graduate, in today's mental health climate, finding a job may be a difficult process, and finding one that pays a living wage may be more than difficult.

When the AATA formed in 1969, its major collective goal was to establish a credible place for art therapy as *a psychotherapeutic mental health discipline* within the hierarchal pantheon of mental health—psychiatry, psychology, social work, and marriage and family counseling. This intention differentiated art therapy from a psychologically informed *educational* pursuit or an activity, recreational or occupational endeavor. From its beginnings, "art therapy" was an *umbrella definition* including many different forms of practice. It remained that way within the new professional organization and within the general art therapy community and, in my opinion, never had a stable unitary identity to present to the larger mental health community and potential consumers.[2] In addition, that art therapy was primarily a woman's profession is not to be discounted and has both explicit and implicit meanings for its development.

Philosophically, I am convinced that the strength of organized art therapy has been exactly in its *inclusiveness of differences.* Functionally, however, these differences—expressed by strong, individualistic and vocal personalities—have often resulted in a competitive battle for power and dominance in the art therapy community, which consumes important energy internally that could be better used elsewhere. Organized art therapy practiced intense *polarization* long before it was ever recognized as an important, hampering part of the national American political scene. At least some of this fighting grows out of art therapy as a woman's profession, in that for many of the founding women, it was not safe to express their strongly felt ideas in an outside male-

---

2. On a TV show this week, I heard the term "art therapy class."

dominated society, and so they did so in the protective environment of art therapy.

University art therapy educational programs were often set up with one theoretical philosophy or other, representing the views of their founders and inculcating their students with that particular philosophy. In many instances, graduates to this day carry on a "battle" that is long over and outdated about what IS art therapy? About 1975, at the end of my first year teaching in the Immaculate Heart College art therapy master's program, I attended the Art Therapy Educators meeting at George Washington University in Washington, D.C. There I watched all the "big names" of art therapy–people whom I had revered as I read and studied their written works–engage in a nasty competitive exercise about their educational programs, attempting to establish that "mine is better than yours." I was so distressed by the downright mean-ness I saw that I didn't go back to any art therapy event for five years! Unfortunately, as far as I can tell, when a collective, cooperative com-munity is so necessary, this competitive spirit persists to this day.

From the art therapy field's original duality of art and psychology came another theoretical duality. Despite the fact that contemporary art therapy actually includes a number of different theoretical ap-proaches and has broad applicability (Rubin, 2001), and although art therapy always contained a variety of paths toward healing, two major theories both based in Freudian psychodynamic ideas emerged to dominate the field.

When the American Art Therapy Association was formed in the late 1960s, the predominant theory was by Margaret Naumburg, whom many call "the mother of art therapy." In the 1940s, she defined the field as *a separate mental health discipline* and was its first theoretician. Naumburg's (1966) theory posits an *art psychotherapy* in which the art functions as symbolic communication within the therapeutic relation-ship between client and therapist. The art therapist is a *trained psycho-therapist* employing creative methods within a psychotherapeutic pro-cess. In Naumburg's theory, the art product as an aesthetic object is downplayed; it is seen as "symbolic communication." Verbal explo-ration is important in this theory.

A second theory for the field emerged in 1958. Edith Kramer pro-posed *art as therapy* and focused on the creative process as the major healing factor. Kramer placed more emphasis on the art product than had Naumburg. According to Kramer, the "completeness" of the art acts as an indicator of a successful "sublimation"[3] process and therefore illuminates success of the creative process as therapy. Kramer's ideas posited an essentially *nonverbal process,* in which verbal exploration was not key or even desired. Close to art education, Kramer maintained she was not a psychotherapist and did not want to be one, although later she said that she didn't think she and Naumburg were so far apart.

Instead of folding the two theories into each other, they functioned as opposite ends of a continuum—not unlike nature/nurture—and usually ended up in opposition to each other. Art therapists lined up emphasizing one side or the other, polarizing the field to this day. It became an either/or proposition, with one being right and the other, wrong. Educational programs tended to adhere to one theoretical position or the other and succeeding generations of art therapists adopted one position to the exclusion of the other.

In the years following the founding of the AATA, the primary drive was to connect art therapy to other mental health disciplines, and many believed that *art psychotherapy* was and should be the major thrust of the profession. But within the art therapy community, there began to be negative rumblings that this theory was too close to a medical model of therapy, which was likely to cause a lessening of the importance of art and the creative process. In addition, as time progressed, the psychiatric mental health milieu was changing. Then in 1992, a persuasive article appeared, by an art therapist, giving voice to the "creative process as therapy" people, bringing this theory to the forefront. In "Artist in Residence: An Alternative to 'Clinification' for Art Therapists," Patricia Allen argued that the field—to its detriment—had turned too much toward "clinification." By that she meant art *psychotherapy.* Allen stated that the art part of art therapy had become subsumed in other mental health practices. She said, art therapy existed too much as part of the established mental health system and, some said, had lost its emphasis on art. Allen proposed that art therapy must reestablish art as central; she argued for a studio approach in which the art therapist would invite people into a painting studio, often work-

---

3. "Sublimation" was an unconscious defense mechanism described by Freud. Sublimating aggressive impulses into socially acceptable artistic impulses is Kramer's essential contribution to theory. In later years, Freud's daughter Anna Freud and the ego psychologists redefined sublimation as a normal ego function.

ing on their own art beside the client. Allen's studio arts proposal turned the art therapist from a psychotherapist to a psychologically informed category of artist. This idea appealed to many in the profession who might previously have been artists and to those who believed that one could not be an art therapist without consistently and intensely involving themselves in their own art process. As can be seen in some of the essays in this book, many still hold this assumption in the field today. Never adequately researched, that an art therapist must engage in their own art, seems to have become a truism for the field. The shift may also have appealed to those who were unwilling or unable to learn psychotherapy and integrate it with art. Many began to find ways to emphasize the art processes and products in art therapy–their own and that of their clients–and the studio art model became a major thrust of the field.

With the new drive, the concept that art created in therapy was a therapeutic production, much like a psychotherapeutic verbal production and therefore should be kept *confidential*, took on a less important position. With art therapy's new identity, it assumed many of the trappings of art making, sometimes resulting in exhibits of client art work, which had long been controversial in the field. C. Moon's (2001) book, *Studio Art Therapy: Cultivating the Artist Identity in the Art Therapist*, is an example of this genre. Primary emphasis on the centrality of the therapeutic relationship became diluted as the nature of art therapy identity changed. The art therapy pendulum had swung away from art psychotherapy to the other end of a theoretical continuum where it primarily remains today. This theoretical duality often gave art therapy a decidedly split identity and deeply polarized the art therapy community further.

What are the effects of a polarized identity? To engage in any fight, the combatants must be in the ring together, and it could be said that the level and prevalence of ongoing combativeness in the history of art therapy exhibits a strong sense of caring, commitment, and liveliness. In my opinion, this statement would be true (and may well be true of professional communities generally as they attempt to gain a toehold within an already established professional mental health monolith with often hidden, even unconscious, political and economic goals). But dualities tend to be written "something *versus* something else." One idea is pitted against another, and according to dictionary definitions, "versus" means "against." This philosophy of dialectics posits an eventual synthesis of the two conflicting ideas. I have written before of the need to get beyond the duality of the art therapy field (Junge, 2008). In my opinion, the theoretical duality of art therapy is an outdated and old-fashioned model that causes, (among other things), an unfortunate splitting of the field's professional identity.

To move beyond its polarized stuck-point, art therapy needs to find a more effective model for itself, which can bring the community together and encourage it to act *cooperatively*. Experts at imagery, art therapists need a *new image* for today that is an effective *synthesizing* model to pull people together into a cooperative body rather than separating them. Polarization has produced too much either/or, good/ bad, insider/outsider mentality.

While continuing with a diverse approach to practice, I believe art therapy *must* define a synthesized identity to present to the world. It has long been time. It is certainly time now for art therapists to band together, define themselves and their special core attributes and values, and establish *a cooperative identity* that considers and states its position on art, creativity, psychology, clinical practice, and education. It is time to present a collective identity to the world. Unnecessary and unrealistic is an attempt to establish a unitary identity within the art therapy community. But I believe it is imperative that the "umbrella" of the profession visible to the outside world have written on it an *agreed-on collective and cooperative unitary identity.*

Chapter 2

IMAGES OF IDENTITY

S ome years ago, the logo for the annual AATA conference was what
I call "the multiple personalities model" of identity. Within a gen-
derless figure–something like a gingerbread cookie–discrete sections
were bounded by line and labeled "clinician," "educator," "artist," and
the like. This seemed to me a wrong image for art therapy identity
because it indicated that the different identities within a person were
walled off from one another and were stable and stagnant. Instead, I
envisioned an image of permeable identities and boundaries contained within the limits of an individual's skin. I believed these identities exist in an integrated fashion and could be emphasized and focused on as the individual needed them. As people evolve over time
and as cultural relationships change around them, identities also grow
and change. It is said that the only thing constant in life is change; as
is change, established identity is both consistent and in constant flux.

My primary identity is art therapist, but I have others as well. While
an individual may be a trained and functioning art therapist, I believe
it is rare to find a person who would say that art therapy is their dominant identity, but it is the whole of me. It often depends somewhat on
what age people are when they come to art therapy. Historically, in art
therapy, and until recently–since most had never heard of the profession–this "coming" tended to be rather late. In my own case, I didn't
find the field of art therapy until my 30s and I had had many identities by then, including those of wife and mother of two children. When
I found art therapy, I did not lose my other identities but reintegrated
them into a new whole. That we are of many parts creating the whole

has been given the name "Intersectionality" (this will be discussed more fully later in this section).

Recently, I met a woman who, at midlife, entered an art therapy master's program. Previously, she had many successful years as different kinds of health care providers in another field. What she has never formally been is an *art therapist*. This is what she is currently training for. What happens with identity in this situation? Surely, she doesn't lose her previous experience and identities. Keeping them, they should be a major help to her as she embarks on an art therapy career. Art therapy is not merely an additional skill set tacked on to her previous "self." It is something much deeper and more embracing.

Wise educators training psychotherapists of all stripes want people with "life experience." The term implies having been through good and bad experiences, learned from them and come out on the other side. Although it is not impossible to have plenty of life experience early on in chronological age, it is not likely. Usually life experience is tough to acquire without a certain number of years of life passing. I remember when I was the director of the Art Therapy master's program at Loyola Marymount University. I explored the life experience question with a 21-year-old applicant to the program, whom I thought had had a protected and privileged life to that point. She insisted she had plenty of life experience because she had gotten married a year previously!

Originally, identity was a term of *sameness*. But it has changed considerably since its origins, and the 21st-century term of identity is of a messy and shifting concept. To describe it in words is as if we are trying to stop time or forge a boundaried picture-postcard image of something that is innately fleeting and inherently in flux. The complexity of identity is often discussed as if it were stable, strong, coherent, and continuous and not complex at all. To attempt to make clear what inherently lacks clarity is probably impossible. But I am going to act as if identity is an entity that can be grasped and understood. To change something, what it IS must first be acknowledged. So I am going to try.

Frustratingly transparent and fleeting, there are advantages in attempting to pin an image of art therapy identity down, as it has been, as it is now, and as it needs to be in the future. My belief is that because of inconsistent professional identity/ies and internal arguments in the American art therapy community, over the years, art therapy has had a hard time defining itself to mental health communities and the external world. Because we haven't conveyed our identity well to ourselves and to the external world, I propose we may not have a clear sense of what direction we would like our professional identity to take for the future.

There have been long-standing debates in social movement theory about whether a group-to be recognized as a group-must have a shared identity. I believe it must. First, art therapy must face the necessity to construct a clear and coherent identity. Then it must portray that identity to the external world.

In this book, I argue that the visible face that art therapy presents to the world needs attention. My hope is that the attempt at clarity in this book will make a much-needed dialogue more possible. In this chapter, I describe definitions of personal and professional identity, the concept of intersectionality, and the history and evolution of identity in the art therapy profession. By focusing on what has been and what is, I hope to spur many conversations about what can and should be.

DEFINITIONS OF IDENTITY

Personal Identity

Erik Erikson in the 1950s is usually considered one of the earliest psychologists to be fascinated with identity, and his theory provides a contemporary framework for the nature and characteristics of individual identity. Expanding Freud's five stages of personality growth to eight, Erikson posited a model based on the psychodynamic tradition, of an individual's *self* developing *continuity* through life. Each of Erikson's stages is based on a central crisis and has specific age-essential tasks. The psychological sense of continuity is known as *ego-identity,* sometimes simply called "The Self." When he wrote his first book, *Childhood and Society* (1950), the stages after early adulthood were nebulous without much specific detail. As Erikson grew older and moved through life, he noticed the unique characteristics of each stage and filled out his theory. In later years, he added a ninth stage to the model in his book *The Life Cycle Completed* (1987). Do we call this using one's own "life experience"?

Erikson's theory emphasizes past, present, and future components of the experienced life. It proposes an achievement of balance between personal continuity and the expectations of one's community. His theory, in particular, the "identity crisis," has had a tremendous influence on contemporary developmental concepts and psychotherapy. In my opinion, Erikson's work rescued Freud from probable obscurity. Weinrich (1986) states:

> A person's identity is defined as the totality of one's self construal; in which how one construes oneself in the present expresses the continuity between how one construes oneself as one was in the past and how one construes oneself as one aspires to be in the future. (p. 299)

Olson (2010), in the *Stanford Encyclopedia of Philosophy,* writes, "The persistent question [about identity is]" 'What is necessary and sufficient for a past and future being to be you?'"

"Identity" is a term used to describe the *totality of a person's individuality plus the idiosyncratic things that make that person unique.* The term is found particularly in psychology, sociology, social psychology, and anthropology, and it implies a sharing of a *degree of sameness* with others in a particular area. A psychological identity relates to self-image, self-esteem, and individuality. Individual identity is primarily established through identifications with important others. The individual art therapist's identity is formed through education and training, and especially by relationships with art therapy teachers, mentors, and clinical supervisors. It is also constructed by the swirls and pushes of culture and other varieties of contextual influences.

Art therapy students entering a graduate program have at least some idea of what art therapy identity might be because they have chosen it as the unique education for them. Often art has had a particular meaning in fledgling students' lives; perhaps it has provided an important context for their own healing. Through their education and training as art therapists, they will meet and learn from many significant individuals. These relationships with significant art therapy "others" help form art therapy identity.

These days, because of the realities of state licensing and the necessities of gaining employment, many art therapy programs are called "dual-degree" programs. A dual-degree program is one in which the student art therapist combines art therapy studies with studies in other therapeutic disciplines, which may be better established or recognized and/or are state "licensable." A dual-degree program can have a curriculum that *integrates* art therapy with the "other" discipline and in which all the students in the class are in art therapy training, or it can have separate art therapy and other therapy classes in which there may be art therapy students along with non-art therapy students. There is a good deal of variation here in established art therapy programs nationwide. This approach can make a clear art therapy identity difficult.

When a person finishes a master's degree today, the received degree title is seldom "Art Therapy" and, unfortunately, may not even include art therapy at all. Many of us grew up with the rhyme, "Sticks and stones may hurt my bones, but names can never hurt me." We have come to learn that this is not true; how things are named and called, verbally, can have a major influence on our thinking and feelings, on the formation of personality, and, in this case, on identity.

While dual-degree art therapy graduate programs are typically thought of as a necessary bow to the prevailing winds of reality, achieving a strong art therapy identity within this mixed theoretical and verbal framework is complex and problematic. In a dual-degree program and/or with students from other creative arts or mental health fields, for a variety of reasons, the art therapy student may sometimes find another discipline appealing-sometimes simply because the other is better known and understood and, therefore, less challenging. It may seem understandably appealing to the novice art therapist to have an already established and understood essence of safety, unlike the innovative field of art therapy, which requires risk, a strong measure of energy, a pioneering spirit, and a constant need to explain what an art therapist is and does. An art therapy student connected with and taking classes in another mental health discipline such as marriage and family therapy or counseling, and perhaps sharing classes with other kinds of students, has a complicated time of it to acquire a strong art therapy identity.

In my view, to learn and do art therapy is tougher and takes more energy than traditional "talk therapy," in that the art therapist must learn both art and psychology and how to seamlessly integrate them. During graduate school, art therapy students have a protective cohort of like-minded people, but as graduates go into clinics and the world of employment, they may find themselves the *only* art therapist. They are seldom hired specifically as an art therapist but often because of the *other part* of their degree. In their new career, they find themselves open to tremendous pressures of a steep learning curve, colleagues who may not understand what an art therapist is and terrifically complex cases. These days, because of severe economic constraints and cutbacks, fledgling clinicians may be asked to function without the regular backup, support, and teaching of a senior supervisor who can meet with them weekly and go over all their cases, what they have done, and what they will do. As they begin a new career, they are likely to feel alone and terribly vulnerable.

Without a strong identity and with the current overwhelming number and difficult nature of cases, art therapists can grow lonely, and it becomes all too easy to morph into the "other" of their dual degree predominantly or altogether dropping the art. The art therapy community, which might offer support and encouragement, can seem distant, and with the tremendous difficulties of clinic and casework life, the art therapist understandably may wish for a protecting cocoon. Despite a belief in the benefits and values of creativity in therapy that recently graduated art therapists hold, in their new life, the art may fall away.

Many art therapy programs pay at least some attention to identity issues, but few find ways to grow post-graduate art therapists. I once heard an excellent therapist in Los Angeles asked how long it was after graduation until she knew what she was doing. She answered, "Seven years." In my opinion, a great deal more attention needs to be paid to supporting and developing an art therapy identity through all phases of its evolution.

Professional Identity

Professional identity does not rest on Erikson's definition. It is about a person's *group* interaction and, according to Heller (2012) is about "us-ness" rather than "me-ness." The construction of identity can be seen in occupational settings, overall quality of life, and concerns the visibility of a field (e.g., how can the field be seen as distinct from other fields?). How can it convey these distinctions? For art therapy, how is a unique identity constructed, maintained, and conveyed? "Us-ness" is an "objective social category, used as a framework to bring unity within a group" (Heller, 2012, p. 87).

How is Professional Identity Constructed?

Professional identity becomes constructed as a student gains an understanding of the field they are preparing for. It concerns learning a particular set of core attitudes, attributes, and beliefs that will be maintained within the work context after graduation. These relate to what makes the profession special: An important question must be asked and answered: "How can art therapy differentiate itself from other professions?" During the process of becoming a professional, as fresh role behaviors are acquired, new views of the self come into being and are integrated or replace the old. Scottish psychologist Rowena McElhinney (2008) conducted a study of professional development in child psychology trainees. She delineated six categories particularly important to the evolution of professional identity and stated that at times it is natural that all can promote a kind of disequilibrium and ambiguity. These categories are:

1. Perceived competence
2. Formal status
3. Comparisons of self with others
4. Expectations of others
5. Role conflict
6. Role ambiguity (p. 2)

McElhinney's point is that to achieve professional identity, the individual must find her or his way through this fuzziness and imbalance to discover *an appropriate balance* between *the formal status of the role* and the person's perceived *confidence* in that role. It is important to realize that *confidence* is an essential part of the success and strength of identity.

How Is Professional Identity Maintained?

Professional identity is *about knowledge not practice,* and it is about retaining ownership of what is inherently a movable and incomplete body of knowledge. As we go, we must continue to develop our special knowledge base. A knowledge base is defined as the core of training and the acquisition of applied experience. Growing and supporting our own unique knowledge base as art therapists is necessary if we wish to have a strong identity that can be sustained over time. In

"Psychologists as Practitioners, Not Technicians," Rodgers (1966) asserts the need "to be distinctive in one's knowledge base in order to be distinctive in practice" (p. 143). Practice must flow from identity, he says, rather than the other way around.

The AATA, art therapy's major professional organization, was established in 1969, and art therapy as a formal profession began. Art therapy literature that has been forthcoming over the succeeding years has primarily focused on clinical casework exemplifying that art therapy can be useful with a variety of populations and ages. I wonder whether much of the clinical literature also tends to portray the idea to others in mental health that art therapy is about techniques and that they can pick up art "recipes" for use in their own cases. Most art therapy education, historically and today, concerns the training of *practitioners,* is at the master's level, and is predominantly taught by master's-level faculty. Until recently, the terminal degree in art therapy was the master's. Yet developing the knowledge base of a field is predominantly accomplished through research, and the master's is not a research degree. Art therapists in master's education have usually not been adequately prepared to do research and may even be frightened of it, thinking they are artists not scientists and that these disciplines are not even remotely connected. Research training has generally been dropped from mental health master's programs nationwide in favor of doctoral-level research training.

Doctoral-degree education includes intense research training, and the PhD[1] is a research degree. In addition, for the last 20 years or so, to be hired as a tenure-track (continuing) faculty in a university, a PhD from an accredited institution is required. Until relatively recently, the few art therapists earning PhDs were in programs of other disciplines. The only art therapy degree doctoral title that I know of was previously at the Union Institute and University[2] a distance learning institution (before distance learning was ubiquitous).[3] Currently, as far as I know, there are doctorates at Lesley College in "Creative Arts Therapies," Drexel University (formerly Hahnemann Medical College) in

---

1. A PsyD or the equivalent is a professional degree, meaning that it is for post-master's training of clinicians, not researchers, and is usually thought of as somewhat lesser than the PhD.
2. In 2002, due to an Ohio Board of Regents report critical of Union's lack of rigorousness in doctoral studies, there was a reorganization, and a new PhD in interdisciplinary studies was established. The original degree of "Art Therapy" was abolished.

"Creative Arts Therapies," and a PhD or EdD in Art Education with a Specialization in Art Therapy from Florida State University. There is also a Professional Doctorate in Art Therapy at Mount Mary College, which, in three years, provides additional administrative and organizational skills for the clinician but does not specifically focus on research.

In 1993, Debra Linesch and I published an article, "Our Own Voices: New Paradigms for Art Therapy Research," calling for art therapists to produce both qualitative and quantitative research from their own special creative drives and proclivities. These days, there is a call in the field for quantitative research, which many art therapists consider to be "scientific" and therefore more "objective," truth in order to "prove" the effectiveness of art therapy, and thereby, it is thought, make employment and licensing easier. I believe this is a misunderstanding of how mental health disciplines as political and economic entities work.

While there have been obvious exceptions in the art therapy literature, 1969, when the AATA was formed, was 45 years ago, and it is well time that the field got onto developing its knowledge and theory base instead of the continuous attempts at explaining, in the literature and elsewhere, what art therapy is and what art therapists do.

What Image of Professional Identity is Shown to the World?

Tracy McLaughlin in the *Newsletter of the Minnesota Art Therapy Association* (June 12, 2012) expresses art therapy's dilemmas and her own:

> [We are] still fighting to forge an identity that is separate and serious, that can't be filled by volunteer artists, the occasional art-focused occupational group or covered by traditional therapists that know art techniques. I feel I have been having this conversation my entire art therapy life. (p. 1)

On its website, the AATA (2011, 2013) defines *art therapy* as "a mental health profession that uses the creative process of art making to improve and enhance the physical, mental and emotional well-being of

---

3. See Malchiodi's essay (Chapter 4, this volume) regarding the potential hiring problems of art therapy programs adopting Council for Accreditation of Counseling and Related Educational Programs (CACREP) standards.

individuals of all ages" (p. 1). Art therapists are "professionals trained in both art and therapy" (p. 1).

As stated before, the art therapy community does not have a unitary identity but rather an "umbrella" covering a collection of disparate, sometimes contradictory notions of what art therapy is and how to do it, held together by the common thread of artistic creativity integrated with psychology. The AATA states:

> Our culture is one of inclusion of people of all backgrounds, open to new concepts and artistic expression that continues to expand the effectiveness of art as a healing therapy. (p. 1)

With the many ideas about what art therapy is, what image is visible on the art therapy "umbrella" now and what should it be? Because there are as many different varieties of art therapy, as there are different varieties of creativity, along with the ubiquitous internal arguments, to come together to present a consistent picture to the world has been a particularly difficult endeavor for art therapy. As a new kid on the block, art therapy has pulled itself up by its boot straps and, in my opinion, has been too eager to borrow from other fields and theories. Its apparent willingness, these days, to connect to counseling is an example. While this borrowing may sometimes be necessary, it tends to make art therapy seem like a mere application–a "modality"–even a technique, which it is not.

We know how difficult it is to define art in words. We know how difficult it is to truly discuss creativity at anything beyond a surface level. But explaining art therapy is a major part of an art therapist's challenge. When people ask me what an art therapist does, I give an example rather than attempting to provide a verbal definition. (I know a well-known art therapist who said she was tired of explaining what she did to seatmates on airplanes, and she had decided to say she was a "housewife"). We all know the old jokes about helping art therapy graduate students explain their field. But the time to provide a stable vision of our "umbrella" identity is unquestionably *now*.

In my opinion, it is urgent that an image of the art therapy profession be crafted to portray the profession to the "outside" world. This image must be based on our own criteria. Instead of trying to be like the "other" or to be what the other determines us to be, we must decide on and present a sustained and continuous identity to the world.

I began in art therapy before there was art therapy education on the West Coast of the United States. I taught art therapy education in four institutions and directed the master's program at Loyola Marymount University in Los Angeles. Periodically, I still teach. I developed curriculum and faculty, struggled with students who were struggling, and directed more than 300 student master's theses. But my own masters-level education was in Social Work. In a real sense, I came to art therapy as an immigrant, and I believe my "outsider" status may have provided an advantage because I had no trouble "seeing" and immediately understanding the value of art therapy. Sometimes when one is within, it is more difficult to see all the way to the edges. Standing outside may give a clearer perspective.

Today, it may be the immigrant to America who can more clearly see the possibilities of living their expectations, better than those of us born here who may be endlessly disappointed when promises are not kept. It is not without meaning that we currently have a president whose father came from Kenya and whose mother from Kansas, who lived most of her life internationally. As an "immigrant" outsider, I could wade through the complexities of identity and see the expanse of the field of art therapy to its boundaries with clarity and depth of vision. Being an outsider gave me the ability to appreciate the unique pleasures and potentials of the field in a manner that many "insiders" might not be able to see as they grapple with the realities of becoming and being an art therapist. When the great psychologist, Erik Erikson, fleeing Hitler's Germany came to the United States in 1934 at the age of about 32, he was an immigrant, an artist, and a teacher of art who didn't even have a bachelor's degree.

Intersectionality

Intersectionality is a feminist sociological method of studying the relationships of multiple dimensions of personality. A second-order feminisism term, "intersectionality" was originated by Kimberle Crenshaw in 1989 as a critique of feminist theory, which, to that time, held that gender was the most important factor in determining a woman's fate (McCall, 2005). The prevailing idea of the early days of the late 20th-century Women's Movement, which considered women as a homogenous category sharing the same life experiences, was critiqued and disputed by women of color. As a theory, intersectionality began as an inquiry into society's oppression of women, but it is now applied to everybody.

The theory of Intersectionality agues that multiple dimensions of identity such as gender, race, class, social relationships, social organizations, and institutions *function together* to determine a woman's destiny. A personality dilemma is not usually determined by a single identity but by several together that can also function in tension with each other. For example, the classic axes of oppression within society—racism, sexism, homophobia, and religion-based bigotry—do not exist independently of each other but create an interrelated system of multiple forms of discrimination, which ultimately change a woman's experience and identity.

According to scholar Leslie Collins (1986), a marginalized group "often gains a status of being an 'other.'" "Others" are virtually anyone differing from the society schema of an average white male. Writer Audre Lord calls these "the mythical norm" (cited in Collins, 1986, p. 518). As Lord suggests, differences can become oppressive measures for women. Collins designates these intersections of inequality "the matrix of domination" and "vectors of oppression and privilege" (p. 204).

What does Intersectionality have to do with the field of art therapy? Plenty. One could critique the art therapy community and its leading institutions on the grounds of race, class, and privilege, not to mention sexism and homophobia. It is well known that many of the female pioneer art therapists were invited into the mental health landscape and mentored by men, often psychiatrists (Junge, 2010). However, in these paragraphs pertinent to Intersectionality, I will focus only on gender and sexism—art therapy as a woman's profession.

Women have come a long way since the days when I did a research study on women in their 40s and presented it with my writing partner at a social work conference (Junge & Maya, 1985). I remember that the panel chairperson (a woman) congratulated the two men in the audience for coming. (Except for the two, the audience of about 35 was totally women.) Social work, of course, has had a well-known history as a women's profession. In current society, women have still not gained equality in pay or any other way. Sexism and gender bias are prevalent, and, unfortunately, sexism is not a uniquely male endeavor. It is in the air we breathe and in the culture that surrounds and molds us, and it is consciously and unconsciously expressed by both men and women. In employment, promotion, and pay, women still lag behind men. For the reader who wants to know more, I have written a chapter "Art Therapy as a Women's Profession" in my book, *Mourning, Memory and Life, Itself, Essays By an Art Therapist* (Junge, 2008).

Myra Levick, a founder of the AATA and its first president, said to me, "IF [she had doubts about it being one] art therapy is a women's field, what does it matter?"[4] A good question, but there is no doubt that art therapy is a women's profession. I believe it is crucial to consciously recognize the meaning of its being one so that we may move past the inherent power imbalances and discrimination and celebrate art therapy's triumphs in the face of considerable sexism in America.

Organized art therapy was established at a time when middle-class white women were told that to "be good girls" (and "girls" they were called), they needed to stay home and be a wife and mother. It was thought then that a woman's identity was all about nurturing and, in particular, nurturing a marriage and children. The few professional women there were in those times were called bad names and thought to be unfortunately aggressive and inadequate as "normal" women. A family story I grew up with in the 1950s was humorist James Thurber's "A woman's place is in the wrong."

Forty years ago, in its thinking and conceptualization of problems– believing that a child's environment was central in the nature/nurture conflict, the mental health field was dominated by men and male thinking. Mother bashing was rampant–the "schizophrenogenic" mother and her supposed impact should not be forgotten. If a child was having problems, it was typically considered the mother's doing; fathers were seldom mentioned. Art therapy's almost entirely female pioneers ignored the prevailing edicts and provided a model of courage in the face of adversity and encroaching sexism.

Despite the fact that there is still little convincing research to support the claim, stereotypically, women are supposed to be relational and nurturing (and so are therapists). The first generation of art therapy's founders and theorists was anything but. These were tough, outspoken

---

4. A 2003 AATA membership survey found that 91.3% were female, 6.2% were male, and 2.5% did not specify (Elkins, Stovall, & Malchiodi, 2003). In an informal count of AATA membership in the 2004–2005 roster, I found 94.8% were female (Junge, 2008).

women willing to take a stand and fight for it. Living within the strong discriminatory winds of sexism, transformed to internalized sexism, they must have experienced severe wounds to identity both personally and professionally. Feminist therapists have proposed that in psychotherapy, the cultural domination of women as a power imbalance must be a part of therapy because all-too-often, women see their troubles as entirely their own "fault" and of their own making. Women regret that they didn't achieve more and often carry a lack of confidence about what they have achieved. They may experience lowered self-esteem and a desperately crippled identity. The image of the "glass ceiling" as an invisible barrier through which women can see but can't reach didn't come along until 1986.[5] It could be argued that this lack of recognition of the crippling tides of sexism may have enabled art therapists to keep moving forward and, thus, may have been ultimately positive in an "If-I-don't-know-I-can't-do-it, I-do-it-anyway" frame of thinking.

But times are different today. To recognize internalized sexism as an innate portion of art therapy's history is to have a better understanding of where art therapy has been, what it has been up to, and what it has been up against. To recognize the cultural oppression that gives rise to internalized sexism as it intersects with art therapy's identity is to be more fully cognizant of the difficulties art therapy and art therapists have had to encounter to survive. I wrote, "In my opinion, art therapy as a woman's profession should be frankly acknowledged and praised, not hidden in the closet. I consider it something to be proud of and am pleased to be a part of" (Junge, 2008, p. 202).

ART THERAPY IS A NEW PROFESSION

Everybody knows that dual-natured art therapy is a combination of art and psychology. Probably emerging from art therapy's major theorists with their different views about the character and quality of art in art therapy, there has been a long and, at times, vituperous argument over whether psychology or art should take the most prominent

---

5. Although it had been used before, the term is thought to have been coined in an article in a 1986 *Wall Street Journal.* In 1991, it was used by the Department of Labor in a study of Fortune 500 companies.

position in art therapy. Recently, in an e-mail, a first-year art therapy student asked me whether I considered myself an artist or a therapist.

Although the evidence is shaky, many today seem to consider that an art therapist is another form of artist, and it is common wisdom and a basic truth in the field that without consistently doing art, the art therapist can't be qualified and effective. One's understanding of the character of art therapists and their community has distinct ramifications for art therapy identity.

The concept of art therapist identity could be interpreted as both artist and psychologist, but I am advancing a different concept of art therapist. *I propose that the trained art therapist is neither an artist nor a therapist, but both and neither.* **I propose that art therapy is a separate and wholly new field,** different from all others in the mental health arena. Art therapists hold strong interests in both art and psychology and, through education and training, *integrally* employ both in psychotherapy. They learn the qualities and uses of media, the processes of assessment and treatment planning, the uses of art and the creative process as therapeutic interventions to help the client. They learn about timing in therapy. Most importantly, they learn the complicated business of deeply integrating art and psychology *into a new whole.* Prominent art therapist Harriet Wadeson made art throughout her cancer treatment in *Journaling Cancer in Words and Images: Caught in the Clutch of the Crab* (Wadeson, 2011). In her essay for this book, she writes:

> Does the power of this experience [art making while undergoing cancer treatment] tell me that every art therapist should be an artist? I don't think so. But I do believe that to encourage patients and clients to make art and to find it meaningful, art therapists must know that experience for oneself. I don't think a weekend art-making workshop will do it.

In the early 1970s, when I was in a social work master's program, I attempted to use art exercises with clients. I was a trained and passionate artist with years of art information, education, and experience in my background, and I had learned psychotherapy in graduate school. This didn't make me an art therapist because I had not learned how to deeply integrate art and therapy. Nobody taught me in school, and I apparently couldn't do it by myself–I sure tried. Well intentioned I was, but because I didn't know what I was doing, the art exercises I used with patients were awful and just that-exercises. They were *not* a deeply integrated art therapy practice but a poorly understood attempt to use art in therapy. I like to say that Helen Landgarten saved the world from me when she saw my horrible attempts and took me on as an apprentice. Under her wing, it took a lot of disequilibrium and was more than a full year before I became an art therapist who understood what she was attempting to do and could often do it.

Being an artist is different from being an art therapist. Plenty of art therapists are terrible artists but are good art therapists. Plenty of art therapists are not making art but are good art therapists. What *is* necessary is not the talent and ability to create art but the intimate knowledge of the creative process and its vicissitudes in oneself and the willingness and ability to give that to another. There is always the danger of "envy" of the creativity in the client—a naturally occurring form of countertransference—in that the therapist is helping the client make art while they are usually not.

This is not to say that there aren't some art therapists who function as professional artists with the talent and commitment necessary for creative achievement and an artist's career. But most don't. Far more common, especially these days, are the people who majored in psychology or art and were interested in the other. When they found the field of art therapy, it seemed to combine both their interests and promised a career of personal interest and pleasure. Art prerequisites for entry into an art therapy educational program are minimal, and there are some applicants for whom this is the only art experience they have had. Many believe that art therapists and artists are the same and are interchangeable, sometimes resulting in the hiring of artists instead of art therapists. The level of education and experiences of a trained art therapist are often unknown or misunderstood by the public, resulting in confusing the two.

I have had a number of professional artists as art therapy students. But the narcissistic perspective naturally held by an artist is usually difficult for the artist trying to become an art therapist. One left the master's program in the first few months because, she said, making art herself was too important, and she could not put it aside to become an art therapist. Another graduated but went back to her art full time. Another has a thriving art therapy practice with professional art as an equally important sideline. Still another, who has functioned as a professional artist for many years, has embarked on art therapy education because she hopes for a more stable life.

Being a committed artist may even make it difficult to become an art therapist (as it sometimes is for teachers). We know artists are passionate about art. But over time, I have learned that they tend to place creativity and madness[6] close to each other (as did Freud) and may believe that creativity emerges from madness or disequilibrium. They shy away from "analysis" or psychotherapy, fearing that if the madness is "cured," the need for art making will disappear. Consider how this might play out in art therapy training. I wonder about this idea as an underlying countertransference issue for art therapists.

A main interest of mine has been the relationship of art therapists to their own art. I have written before (Junge, 2008) about many art therapists feeling they are "abandoning their art" as they undertake art therapy studies. In 2005, Harriet Wadeson and I gave a presentation at the annual AATA conference on a research study of retired art therapists. Study participants expressed a great deal of guilt over not doing "enough" art. Guilt seems to me not only a female proclivity but perhaps an art therapist's milieu as well. Art therapists' guilt tends to congeal around their own art-not doing it, not doing *enough* of it—a position that many in the field support.

Years ago when there were few jobs for women, they were often told to go into teaching. I wonder whether art therapy may have become one of those "possible" jobs for women who perhaps didn't have the talent or drive necessary to tackle the professional art community, which, even today, is very much a man's world. (Check numbers of exhibiting women artists for evidence.)

On the other side of the coin, talk therapists and counselors, looking for new ways to help clients, may stumble onto art therapy or even seek it out. They tend to emphasize a variety of exercises as add-ons, hoping to help a client express feelings and open up more readily. This can be a dangerous business, in that opening up and the expression of feelings is not a goal to be desired for all clients at all times. There is a prevailing idea in mental health (and even in the trained art therapy community) that creativity and art making is always a good thing. This

---

6. This juxtaposition of creativity and madness is a long outdated idea. Nevertheless, it retains a firm hold on many artists and others.

is not necessarily the case. Discussing the great photographer Diane Arbus, I wrote:

> As Arbus' creative urgency loosened the ego's frail constraints and plunged her deeper and deeper into her unconscious processes her personality shattered . . . her photographic work increasingly drove her into psychologically dangerous territory. (Junge, 2008, p. 105)

Many mental health professionals may not believe there can be significant psychological danger caused by clients making art. But for therapists who do not understand the dangers of the creative process or concepts of "timing" in psychotherapy, art making can pose real difficulties to the vulnerable client's ability to carry on with enough stable personality structure to continue functioning in the world. The good thing about art is it confounds defense mechanisms to go right to the suffering heart and psyche. The bad thing about art is it escapes defense mechanisms and goes right to the suffering heart and psyche. An example is that many therapists may ask clients, particularly children, to "Draw your family." Often done in a first session, this is intended to give the therapist information. As an art intervention, it is certain to cause anxiety in the client—perhaps tremendous anxiety. There is not one of us who could draw our family, no matter how functional, without anxiety rising in us. While the exercise may provide important information for the therapist, so as not to hurt the client or hinder the evolving therapeutic relationship, art's introduction into treatment must come with knowledge and a careful consideration of timing. A well-trained art therapist will know the difference and how and when to use art interventions for maximum benefit for the client. A therapist or an artist using art exercises as mere technique is not likely to even understand that there *is* a difference and could easily cause harm. A tenet of the profession should be to caution about the dangers of unbridled, unknowing, and misunderstood creativity.

Art therapy as a profession, while clearly culling from art on the one hand and psychology and psychiatry on the other, is neither one nor the other. Instead, it is a seamless *integration* of the two, which, I believe, *forms a new whole.* As the systems people like to say, to put together all parts of a cow does not necessarily a cow make: The whole is greater than the sum of its parts. So it is with art therapy. The core values and attributes of art therapy are centrally important, but the way they come together to make something special, different, and new is crucial.

As the sum is greater than the parts, so art therapy's *identity to the external world must center around the new whole.* While inside art therapy's umbrella there can be diverse definitions, the image of a shared public identity art therapy portrays to its community and especially, to the outside–potential clients and the mental health professions–should be clear, compelling, and simple enough to be readily understood. And it is necessary that it first be reasonably understood by art therapists as well.

A SHORT HISTORY OF IDENTITY IN ART THERAPY[7]

In his song, "This Land Is Your Land," Woody Guthrie writes of the expanse of America as "California to the New York Islands." So, too, the evolution of the innovative field of art therapy in the United States has been a widely spreading proposition. Art therapists range from the Pacific to the Atlantic Oceans and include the Midwestern states in between. In the early days, knowing no others like them, many lone art therapists thought they invented the practice themselves. Often they were artists who learned psychological theories and methods on their own and integrated them with their knowledge of the visual arts. The dilemma of "Are you an artist?" or "Are you a therapist?" has been a consistent theme throughout art therapy's history, symbolically representing a split identity and the competitive "either/or" conflict within the field.

Margaret Naumburg, art therapy's first great theorist, born in New York City, is thought to have defined the field in about 1940, calling it "dynamically oriented art therapy" and establishing it as a separate mental health discipline. Before that, in 1925, in Topeka, Kansas, the Menninger Foundation was founded. First a sanitarium and later a major center for psychiatric training and milieu therapy, from its inception, Menninger gave important presence to art. Mary Huntoon set up an arts program at Winter Veteran's Hospital, and at Menningers, art

---

7. For a detailed history and cultural context of art therapy, see my book, *The Modern History of Art Therapy in the United States* (Junge, 2010).

therapy pioneers Don Jones and Robert Ault were art therapists in the institution (both were painters), and many generations of art therapists were trained and employed at Menninger.

In 1941, Naumburg went to work for psychiatrist Nolan D. C. Lewis at the New York Psychiatric State Institute, functioning as an adjunct psychotherapist with children and adults and treating patients along with their psychiatrist. Her book describing her theory, *Dynamically Oriented Art Therapy* (1966) was published when she was 84 years old.

Edith Kramer, the other major art therapy theorist, published her first book in 1958. It is based on her work at the Wiltwyck Home for Boys, a residential treatment center in upstate New York. Whereas Naumburg's theory focuses on the art product as symbolic communication and therefore not a substantial piece of art, Kramer proposes that the creative process itself is healing and that the complete and fully formed art product represents the success of sublimation and the art therapy. Naumburg's ideas are about art *in* psychotherapy; Kramer's are about art *as* therapy, and she was well known as standing up at the yearly AATA conferences to decry the loss of art in art therapy practice. Both Naumburg's and Kramer's concepts are based on Freudian psychodynamic thinking, but Kramer is closer to psychologically informed art teaching whereas Naumburg is akin to clinical psychotherapy.

Elinor Ulman created the first art therapy journal, *The Bulletin of Art Therapy,* in 1961. Later its name was changed to the *American Journal of Art Therapy.* In 1963, Ulman found only 30 art therapists in the United States and Canada. Ulman's establishing of a journal was crucial and an incredibly coalescing force for the new field. It provided lonely art therapists a place to communicate and argue ideas and it offered a place to publish in which those ideas, could maintain a concrete and consistent presence. This first journal of art therapy was in existence from 1961 to 2002–41 years (Junge, 2010).

The professional organization for art therapy, the American Art Therapy Association, was founded in 1969. Invited by psychiatrist and founder Irene Jakab, many art therapists had previously attended the conferences of the International Society for the Psychopathology of Expression and the American Society for Psychopathology of Expression. The Societies focused on art expression as an important window into patient pathology. Art therapists were officers, presenters at the

Societies' conferences, and they published papers in Jakab's volumes. This presence gave art therapists credibility as experts and, most importantly, brought them together. But the Societies were primarily dominated by psychiatrists, and according to art therapy pioneer Don Jones, art therapists felt like "invited guests" (Junge, 2010, p. 13). Eventually, they decided to form their own organization where art therapists would be in charge, would be voting members, and where, along with pathology in art, treatment issues could be explored.

From its beginnings, the AATA was an inclusive organization with a broad definition and identity. It was also an organization of loudly espoused contradictory positions and an either/or, good/bad competitive atmosphere. The two major "teams" were art psychotherapy clinicians and art therapists from education and rehabilitation. Elinor Ulman and Edith Kramer, among others, originally thought forming an organization was premature and were concerned that the new organization would be too psychotherapeutic in nature and too controlled by psychiatrists. They proposed that art therapy "look to an independent place in the broad field of special education and rehabilitation" (Junge, 2010, p. 105). In many quarters, the competitive split still exists today generations later.

The first president of the AATA, Myra Levick, was a clinician, and the first Honorary Life Member award was accepted by Margaret Naumburg, also a clinician. Although the early leaders of AATA held different job titles in their home institutions, many considered themselves psychotherapy clinicians. The constitution of the new organization mandated entry level for art therapists at the master's-degree level, putting the new field on a par with other mental health disciplines and establishing it as post-Baccalaureate and as needing specific professional education and training. In her announcement of the new organization, President Levick wrote:

> For the past 20 years artists have been involved in using their skills to aid in the diagnosis and treatment of psychiatric patients. . . . It is an established fact that an organization must be formed in order to attain professional recognition. And it is with great pleasure that we announce that the AATA [The American Art Therapy Association] was voted into being on June 27, 1969 in Louisville, Kentucky, by a representative group of art therapists from all over the country and Canada. The goals of this new group go far beyond merely formalizing that which has

already been achieved. It is hoped that Art Therapy and its relation to mental health and education will be more clearly defined and further developed. (Levick in Junge, 2010, p. 107)

Although there was plenty of alarm that it would create a premature narrowing of the field, AATA quickly established Standards of Practice and a Registration process (ATR) for those art therapists meeting those standards. It was a time of financial expansion and innovation in the United States, and to train future generations, many art therapy pioneers founded educational programs in universities and colleges across the country, and a few training programs originated in hospital psychiatric settings. Thus, art therapy's first identity was as a fledgling but special *mental health discipline.* Even those not working specifically in psychiatric settings were defined as *clinicians.*

Many Eastern art therapists were adjunctive members of the treatment team for inpatient psychiatric patients. Hana Kwiatkowska, credited with "inventing" family art therapy, and Harriet Wadeson were employed at the National Institute of Mental Health in Bethesda, Maryland—part of the prestigious National Institutes of Health. They functioned as researchers with psychiatric patients and their families. Following Mary Huntoon, painters Don Jones and Robert Ault became art therapists at the Menninger Foundation in Topeka. In 1959, Spanish psychiatrist Pedro Corrons established the first state-supported art psychotherapy department at Columbus State Hospital in Ohio. He was joined by art therapist Bernard Stone. Myra Levick was an art therapist on an inpatient unit at Albert Einstein Hospital in Philadelphia. She later founded and directed the first art therapy master's program in the country at Hahnemann Hospital and Medical Center.[8] In California, Helen Landgarten worked first on an inpatient unit at Los Angeles County/USC Hospital and then at Cedars Sinai Medical Center, Thalians Community Mental Health Center, where she pioneered art therapy with outpatient clients. She coined the term "clinical art therapy." Her master's program at Immaculate Heart College, Hollywood, California, trained students as "clinical art therapists" or primary therapists, which meant they were able to function equally with other mental health professionals and to carry full case responsi-

---

8. Now "Drexel."

bility rather than be an adjunctive member of a treatment team, typically led by a psychiatrist.

For 23 years, art therapy's major thrust and identity, both within the profession and externally, was as a mental health discipline, like social work, psychology, and psychiatry. But the mental health system in America was changing: Psychiatric hospitals were being shut down, starting with President John Kennedy's community mental health act (which intended to increase the outpatient treatment of patients in their own communities), and gaining intensity during Ronald Reagan's presidency. The efficacy of traditional psychiatric "talk" therapies was questioned, and behaviorism gained sway in psychiatric clinics and institutions. Few, if any, art therapists were behaviorists.

In the 1990s, art therapists increasingly secured employment with non-clinical populations–like the homeless–often with personal growth as the major goal, and they were finding payment through grants. Within the art therapy community, complaints were made that psychiatric art therapy was too focused on the medical model, which looked for pathology and diagnoses. Edith Kramer maintained she was not a psychotherapist, nor did she want to be one. In addition, for a long time, there had been strong rumblings in the profession that the art in art therapy had lost its importance; it was thought crucial by many that art therapists must continue their personal artwork to be able to adequately function as a clinician. As forms of behaviorism gained dominance in psychiatric institutions and clinics, because of health insurance and other restrictions, short-term therapies–sometimes as little as one or two sessions–became prevalent. In art therapy, community service treatment approaches with specific populations took over, and the importance of the creative process and art-making assumed a renewed precedence. Within educational programs, students spent increased time in art-making activities.

For the last 20 years or so, the identity of the art therapist has been that of a special kind of artist. In her essay in this book, Harriet Wadeson writes: "I think art therapists get themselves into trouble when they apply 'either/or' definitions. I believe art therapy can embrace many ways of working which need not compete with each other." Even within an "either/or" atmosphere, it could have been argued that the new focus on art making and the creative process was a necessary bending to the realities of the overwhelming changes in the mental health system and a good thing. But this attitude was never acknowl-edged or, do I believe, consciously understood. Instead, the swing toward the "art as therapy" end of the pendulum was promoted as a necessary theoretical emphasis and a moving forward for art therapy. This narrow definition, often viewed as "good" while the art psycho-therapy model is "bad" along with the ubiquitous dual-degree issue (to be fully discussed later in this book), has promoted considerable diffi-culty in the art therapist's ability to achieve a coherent identity. In par-ticular, the visible face that the field shows to the external world—the "image on the umbrella"—presents a confusing picture because, I be-lieve, art therapy has been confused itself.

Part of the problem is that every 2 years, the major professional leadership organization, the AATA, has a new president, and where the last president may have moved in one direction, the incoming president may take an entirely different approach. One example is that a few presidents pushed that art therapy become a subgroup of counseling. (I am told this is no longer true, but the perception that this issue is ongoing still persists among membership.) Another example: Almost 10 years ago, art therapy was placed in the Department of Labor's list of occupations as an "adjunct" category and a bachelors-level *activity*-focused discipline. This was called a "mistake" by a prom-inent art therapist, and the AATA is now attempting an arduous pro-cess to get art therapy removed from the adjunct, bachelors-level cat-egory, placing it with other master's-level mental health disciplines.

The original founders of art therapy worked to establish a profession grounded in the traditions and practices of psychotherapy. In the last decades, the leadership of art therapy's major professional organiza-tion apparently has shifted emphases with each new president. Per-ceptions still prevail of art therapy pushing to become part of coun-seling and being viewed by the Department of Labor as an activity, recreation, or leisure occupation. In her essay in this book, Malchiodi suggests that art therapy "may be undergoing its own form of identity confusion disorder." It is no wonder that the art therapy community struggles to understand and construct a coherent identity for itself and to present it to the world.

Chapter 3

LIVING IN THE REAL WORLD,
ISSUES AND CHALLENGES

THE IMPORTANCE OF WORDS AND
THE CHALLENGE OF DUAL DEGREES

There is not an art therapist alive who doesn't deeply wish that identity for the person and for the field could be expressed through simple and clear words–that is, an individual who assumes the functions of an art therapist and has formal training should be *called an art therapist,* no two ways about it. An educational program that trains art therapists *should give a degree title called "Masters of Arts (or Sciences) in Art Therapy,"* no two ways about it. The art therapy program or department *should be described as "Art Therapy."* Unfortunately, these simple and clear designations are less and less the case and will probably be so for the foreseeable future.

Previously, we thought that words were not important and could not be hurtful or crippling. In Shakespeare's *Romeo and Juliet,* Juliet argues that names do not matter. "A rose by any other name would smell as sweet," she says. Parents advised school children to chant, "Sticks and stones may break my bones, but names will never hurt me." But even back then, school children knew that was not true when they said it. In current reality, language is rightly understood to have power and can be used to indicate dominance. "Hate speech" and "bullying" have been defined and called into question, and the recognition and acknowledgment of the use or misuse of language has led to ubiquitous "politically correct" speech, intended as an improvement.

In order for art therapy graduates to gain employment and to be eligible for state licensing (which helps ensure employment), education programs have needed to assume broader definitions and bend titles, curriculum, and sometimes even department names to suit outside state agencies. This sounds downright shady, like calling Juliet's rose by another name; it's not. It is a matter of recognizing an art therapy graduate's right to work and the pragmatics of the real world in which the field lives. Typically, it is not a matter of substantially changing content or quality but of using specific descriptive *words* to suit designated requirements.

My master's education—pretty much by accident, I really had no idea then what a social worker traditionally did—was in social work at the University of Southern California, a well-respected school. I later directed the graduate art therapy program at Loyola Marymount University in Los Angeles. (There were no West Coast art therapy programs then.) Having experienced two kinds of mental health professionals' education, I know well that art therapy training programs are different from other mental health training programs and sometimes better in clinical training. As one beginning art therapy student put it, "Social work has no art!"

I was a long-time and passionate professional artist when I entered social work school, but I certainly couldn't learn art therapy there. In my first jobs out of school, as an often terrified novice, what I fell back on was what I knew and had learned in school—talk therapy. Although I tried, for me using art in therapy without specific training was not an easy proposition, and I did it badly. Although I was an experienced artist, I couldn't learn art therapy on my own, and it took me quite awhile and concentrated training to integrate art enough to be comfortable and effective with it. Although I was always an art therapist, I was a "dual-degreed" person even then.

In the various clinics I worked in, that I was an art therapist was valued and that is what I functioned as—but I was probably hired as a "social worker" because those words were familiar to administration and Human Resources and listed in the formal mental health hierarchy of professions. I functioned as a staff member in outpatient clinics equal to professionals of other disciplines. Clients usually didn't come to me specifically for art therapy but because I had an opening in my caseload. Then I would say, "We're going to do art. That's how I work. Give it a try."

There is no question that the realities of post-graduate employment need to be a priority for the profession–along with achieving a living wage–but what things are *called* in art therapy cannot help but cause perplexing and confusing identity issues for art therapists and others, including consumers. An art therapist is often hired under another mental health job title such as "counselor" or "psychologist" because the profession of art therapy is not typically recognized as a mental health profession in the occupations code. In a list of the various kinds of mental health practitioners hired in a clinic, large or small, the title of "art therapist" usually doesn't exist. So, at best, an art therapist is often employed as one of the "legitimate" disciplines along with something extra-the art. An additional problem can be that having come in contact with art therapy, many employers view the art in art therapy as something that should be used occasionally or when it seems particularly pertinent, such as when the client is nonverbal. This constitutes a lack of understanding about the nature of art therapy and that it is not merely a nonverbal process. Many art therapy graduates receive diplomas from their universities or colleges, which do not mention art therapy at all or at best call it a "specialization in art therapy." Few university programs or departments are designated "art therapy." Few art therapy faculty are "official" tenure track employees. A "tenure-track professor" as opposed to an "adjunctive professor" means that the university or college has potentially invested in her or him by expecting him or her to stay over the long term. When the program and its faculty are not official parts of the university, it can be abolished at will, and in the last several years, we have seen some of that happen. Some art therapy programs are housed in "Professional Studies" or in a School of Education. These confusing and disparate responses to art therapy by the "outside academic world" have *meaning* for the student and graduate. They add up to create complex identity issues for newly minted art therapists and for more experienced ones.[1] One recent graduate of an art therapy program who stated that her education was "as good as any two-year education could possibly be" goes on to say,

---

1. The art therapy department at Loyola Marymount University, which I directed, was a free-standing entity within the graduate division of the university. When it came time for graduation each May, the university could not figure out where our graduates should march because we were not a member of a college. For a number of years, we marched behind the flag of the College of Liberal Arts, even though we were not officially within it. The ultimate outsider experience!

"I still question my belief in art therapy versus traditional psychother-apy. I identify more as a mental health therapist." In the eye of the hur-ricane, negating art therapy by not clearly naming it for what it is, intentionally or unintentionally, denigrates the profession and is an as-sault on identity. When this happens, it can become difficult for the in-dividual to hold onto a healthy sense of identity, which might solidify into a developing personal and professional art therapy identity and engender an important commitment to the field. Is it any wonder that so many art therapy graduates leave the profession?[2]

With the necessity for their graduates to work, art therapy master's programs must take a pragmatic stance and are increasingly empha-sizing dual degrees, which causes still more identity confusion. What "dual degree" means is that an art therapy program contains curricu-lum (often mandated by the state) that makes the graduate eligible for state therapy licensing because they are not usually eligible with "art therapy" or even "creative arts therapies" alone. Some degree titles are "Art Therapy and Counseling" or "Psychology with Specialization in Art Therapy"; some do not mention art therapy at all. Of 33 American Art Therapy Association approved[3] programs, only about a third grant specific art therapy degrees. The array of different degree titles, names of programs, and positions in the university reflects the diversity of the field and its entry into academia with curriculum committees and Boards of Regents to consider. But highly important to identity is the previ-ously mentioned attempt to create a proper curriculum that will be state-mental-health-license eligible. It is not always simply a curricular problem, but one in which the state licensing board may mandate the degree title resulting in the words "art therapy" sometimes taking a dis-tinct second place or perhaps disappearing altogether. One program director writes, "our curriculum, with the addition of an additional class or two, met [counseling license] eligibility requirements. However, the li-censing board required the word 'Counseling' to be in the degree title."[4]

While a specific state license for art therapists is sometimes talked about, I consider the possibility generally to be a pie-in-the-sky idea—

---

2. I am told that art therapy master's programs are thriving, and three new graduate programs opened this year.

3. The AATA grants in "Approval," a form of accreditation, to those art therapy programs that meet its curricular standards

4. Although the AATA does not endorse dual degrees, they are ubiquitous in art therapy programs today.

at least at this time. Along with the fact that the art therapy field is small and likely to remain so, to bring a state license into being is a long, costly, and usually volunteer *political process* that needs knowledgeable advocates, effective strategies, and the ability to keep going sometimes for years in the face of considerable adversity. Even if art therapy licensing could be brought forward, it is likely that in such a strangled economic climate, the more established and already licensed mental health disciplines might mount considerable opposition to another, joining the crowd and therefore spreading even thinner what is already a small pot. Some years ago, a potential for state licensing existed with the National Coalition of the Arts Therapies (NCATA)[5] which was a group composed of art, dance, music, poetry, and drama associations.[6] Because of its large membership, this organization might have proved a substantial political force toward state licensing. While a joint conference was planned every 2 to 3 years and an AATA president was supportive of the coalition, unfortunately, the next AATA president was not interested, did not support NCATA, and any political potential was lost. One art therapist calls this "Another piece of our self-destructive history" (M. Levick, personal communication, 2012).

The move toward dual degrees to gain state licensing for art therapists should be viewed as commendable recognition of the pragmatics of employment, born out of an appropriate desire to protect graduates and enhance their life, but it creates additional difficulties and complex problems for identity formation that must be recognized, acknowledged, and adequately managed. Art therapy is already a profession of inherent dualism. To pile on dual degrees in which art therapy is typically the secondary designation creates a problem of personal and professional multiple identities in the student or graduate. All too often, the art therapist becomes the "other" and loses art therapy identity and functioning entirely. In his biography of Barack Obama, David Maraniss (2012) describes a teenage Barack, called "Barry" in school:

---

5. The AATA was a member of the Coalition.
6. In about 1985, when California was undergoing revision of its Marriage and Family Counseling psychotherapy licensing laws and there was a good deal of turmoil about the art therapy program within Loyola Marymount University, David Read Johnson, president of NCATA at the time wrote an important and supportive letter that was instrumental in securing a positive outcome for the master's program.

Barry was not the most talkative student. . . . He would sit near the back of the room, relaxed, waiting for his opening. . . One day they were dealing with a philosophical question about what people should most fear. The answers included loneliness, death, hell, and war. Then Barry straightened up . . . "Words," he said. "Words are the power to be feared most. . . . Whether directed personally or internationally, words can be weapons of destruction." (pp. 299–300)

Here we must ask *does* a rose by any other name smell as sweet?

SELF-DEFINITION VERSUS DEFINITION BY OTHERS

When organized art therapy began in 1969 with the founding of the professional organization, the American Art Therapy Association, attracting art therapists from across the country with a diverse variety of approaches, the clear identity of art therapy then was *as a psychiatric mental health discipline.* The forward drive and intention of the AATA was to establish it as such. Recognizing the need to stand with other mental health fields, like them, the AATA delineated Standards of Practice, and a system was created through which an art therapist who met specific standards could become "Registered" (ATR). Later, Board Certification (BC) could be obtained through the passing of an informational exam. The ATR and BC are *national art therapy credentials* given originally by the AATA and now by the Art Therapy Credentials Board and bear no relationship to state licenses. An assessment process for art therapy educational programs came into being, with those meeting standards designated "Approved."

The necessity to become more standardized caused some art therapists to decry the loss of the creativity that had brought the innovative field into being in the first place. Although the dilemma persists to this day, there seemed then a clarity about the art therapist's personal identity and the professional identity of the field. Twenty years or so later, a renewed perspective on placing art and creativity in the forefront came into being in the field, with healing or personal growth as a goal. Less emphasis was placed on psychiatric or clinical art therapy or on the previous searchlight focus of art therapy in psychiatric milieus. At this point, some would say art therapy officially became more diverse. In my opinion, both personal and professional identity grew more complex, more confusing, and more confused.

It is important to remember that from its beginnings, the AATA counted on its members to be volunteers. They gave countless hours and many sleepless nights to accomplish the immense organizational tasks of creating an innovative profession and propelling it forward. (It wasn't until many years later that a professional management firm was hired and took over some of these tasks.) With an organization of over-burdened and changing volunteers trying to do 60 different things at once, a major problem for the field has been institutional and professional *continuity*. There was little, if any, continuity about decision making, and most decisions were verbal and not documented. That a new president of AATA with a new Board of Directors arrived every 2 years, often with a completely different agenda from the last and little memory of the past, didn't help matters. For example, in 1987, when I first proposed to write *A History of Art Therapy in the United States* and thought that it should be published by the AATA, the then president enthusiastically agreed. But as books do, it took awhile. Every time a new president began, it was as if this verbal agreement (which I considered written in stone) disappeared, and I would have to start trying to convince them all over again.[7]

THE DILEMMA OF RESEARCH IN PROFESSIONAL IDENTITY

Research is a method in which a field adds to its knowledge base. Discussing the identity of Industrial Organizational Psychology, in her presidential address, Ann Marie Ryan (2003) states,

> We cannot define ourselves through just a reference to the types of practice we engage in but we must be referring back to our knowledge base and our disciplinary core . . . our identity derives from *how* [italics, mine] we do it, how we approach it, what we base it on. Our identity isn't from our practice. Our practice flows from our identity. (p. 25)

Exactly the same should be said of art therapy.

Until about 25 years ago, requirements for mental health master's programs of all stripes included a research project and a thesis. Due to

---

7. Finally, I managed to get it done, because the AATA president at the time, Bobbi Stoll, enthusiastically supported the project for the AATA's 25th birthday, and the chairman of the Education Committee, Patricia Allen remembered that it had been agreed to and supported it.

the lack of necessary extensive time and resources, the tradition that a master's student design and carry out a research project as a requirement for graduation has largely been abandoned in favor of research in doctoral training; a PhD is a research degree, a master's is not.

Throughout its history, art therapy education at the master's level has predominantly focused on the training of *clinicians,* and it still does. Students do not enter a master's program intending to be anything but a practitioner and seldom, if ever, are they even interested in research of any kind. Nonetheless, the educational standards of the AATA mandate a research course for an approved curriculum containing:

> basic tenets of planning, conducting and evaluating research and understanding research methodology, [including] qualitative and quantitative designs; . . . ethical, practice and legal considerations and the use of research . . . to assess effectiveness of mental health and art therapy services. (AATA Standards, cited in Brennan, 2011, p. 141)

It is unclear whether this mandated course is intended to do anything but familiarize students with research concepts and ideas. What *is* clear is that, like other mental health master's programs, a carefully designed and carried out research project is *not* a requirement of the AATA for program "Approval."

The dilemma of research in art therapy reflects a primary art/ psychology duality. Psychology is thought to be the "hard" science side that many believe conflicts with art and aesthetic practices. Art therapists primarily consider themselves to be "right-brained" people. As such, there has been some reluctance to do research at all in art therapy because it is viewed as "scientific" and "left brained," and many art therapists see themselves as a variety of artist. This skewed notion is based on the old idea that science and art do not mesh, and if one is an artist, innately and genetically one is a completely different breed from a scientist and cannot or should not learn to "do" science. Perhaps also residing in the unconscious is the old idea that understanding too much destroys creativity. Sometimes it is even mistakenly supposed that to be too "objective" may cause creativity to disappear entirely. This misunderstanding, of course, also speaks to the belief that the only research of value is empirical and quantitative.

More than 40 years ago, Thomas Kuhn (1964) published *Structure of Scientific Revolutions,* in which he convincingly argued that even science is not totally objective. "It depended on the interests of the particular researcher who chose what was to be studied," Kuhn wrote (Junge, 2010, p. 277). Although Kuhn's argument caused a paradigm shift in many long-held beliefs about the inevitable immutable stability of the scientific endeavor, the old paradigm still exerts a stranglehold in many quarters. Unfortunately, some reside in art therapy.

Based in another "old hat" misunderstanding, quantitative research assumes that reality and the person are objectively knowable, and causality and predictability result from this method of research as a search for *truth*. In "Our Own Voices: New Paradigms for Art Therapy Research" published 20 years ago, Debra Linesch and I (1993) argued for a variety of ways of knowing that might be more amenable to artistic methodologies:

> the argument is for both the naturalness and the necessity of an expanded range of lenses through which art therapists can approach research.
> . . . The word "research" [to art therapists] too often evokes waves of insecurity and images of scientific laboratories and white coats. This is because it is generally associated with the single predominant paradigm of Western science, positivism and the empirical, quantitative model. (pp. 61 & 62)

A major point of the article was that art therapists can and should *think* and can and should learn to do research. But there are many cultures of inquiry amenable to art therapists.

In a 1992 journal article, "Research Approaches Within Master's Level Art Therapy Training Programs," Linesch reported on a questionnaire assessing attitudes and approaches to research. Not surprisingly, she found that training clinicians was the major goal of master's art therapy education, and the case study method was widely practiced.[8] By 1998, art therapists Gantt (1998), Malchiodi (1995), and Rosal (1998) had "all called for research as a priority in the art therapy profession"(Junge, 2010, p. 276). This call for outcome research

---

8. It is sometimes said by students in art therapy programs that the case study occurs from the failure of "real" research.

seemed to ignore the obvious fact that few master's-level students have the training or inclination to undertake useful research.[9]

As to art therapy research in the intervening years, searching through the archives of the American Art Therapy Association journal *Art Therapy,* I found few research articles. While there may be some writings on research in other journals, judging from the minimal numbers, I believe it is safe to say there is an evident lack of interest or at least publication in research. In 2000, Betts and Laloge published "Art Therapists and Research: A Survey Conducted by the Potomac Art Therapy Association," and Julliard, Gujral, Hamil, and Oswald (2000) presented "Art-Based Evaluation in Research Education." Carolan published "Models and Paradigms of Art Therapy Research" in 2001. In 2002, "What Constitutes Art Therapy Research?" by Deaver was published, and in 2006, "Teaching Art Therapy Research: A Brief Report" by Kaiser, St. John, and Ball appeared. All in all, this is not many.

In recent years, art therapists have proposed a focus for the field that produces careful, systematic (probably quantitative) outcome research in order to "prove" the effectiveness, and therefore credibility, of art therapy. In 2000, Reynolds, Nabors and Quinlin published a review of the literature prior to 1999, "The Effectiveness of Art Therapy: Does It Work?", and in 2010, Slayton, D'Archer, and Kaplan published "Outcome Studies on the Efficacy of Art Therapy: A Review of Findings," reviewing literature from 1999–2007. Citing 35 studies, the authors conclude "that there is a small body of quantifiable data to support the claim that art therapy is effective in treating a variety of symptoms, age groups, and disorders" (p. 108). Frances Kaplan (2000), known as a leading proponent for the potential of good research in the field, has made the case that art therapy can be scientific. I am also told that the AATA plans a future research emphasis for its journal, *Art Therapy.*

While quantifiable, outcome research could add to the knowledge base of the field, the thrust here seems to be a push toward credibility for art therapy within the mental health community and for state licensing for art therapists. It assumes that if art therapy is proven

---

9. Doctoral programs in art therapy in brick-and-mortar, accredited institutions are only now beginning. Union Graduate University (a distance learning endeavor, primarily) from which many art therapists earned their PhD, until recently did not require that students design and carry out a research project at all. Students in the few beginning art therapy doctoral programs have the potential to produce useful research in the future.

effective to the external world-in particular the mental health establishment—the gates to the kingdom (and to state licensing) will open. I
believe this erroneous assumption reflects a naïve confusion about the
reality required to gain licensing. The path to licensing is a *political
process*. It is long and costly, and, unfortunately, it seldom has to do
with effectiveness or quality. Moreover, it is probable that should the
art therapy community be able to show how effective its work is (a
notoriously difficult proposition, in and of itself) and move toward licensing, other mental health disciplines would then mount a considerable campaign against the "interloper." It is hard to imagine them
inviting the new kid on the block in to share what is already thought
to be a pie that is not big enough to go around.

It is well known that an abundance of research action produces both
plenty of bad and, hopefully, some good research. Unquestionably,
good research is necessary for the field and would be a valuable addition to art therapy's knowledge base. As doctoral programs proliferate,
graduating more and more students trained as researchers, there may
come a time when research can provide a useful driving direction for
the profession. But within present constraints, it is simply not a realistic focus. As I see it, it is an overt bow to the identity of the field being
defined externally.

Art therapy is a unique profession with its own core values and attitudes. While straining to be enough "like" the others to be creditable
may be necessary and appropriate, art therapy must define its identity from its special and innovative values and attitudes, finding a way
in which this vision can be proclaimed, portrayed, and celebrated.

ADVANTAGES AND DISADVANTAGES
OF AN UMBRELLA IDENTITY

In her essay in this book, pioneer art therapist Harriet Wadeson praises the diversity in art therapy: "I see no need to categorize ourselves
[as mental health or recreational/rehabilitative]. We are what we do .
. . a one-size-fits-all approach definitely does not apply in art therapy."
I believe one of art therapy's strengths has been its many different
approaches. To name a few, the art therapist can function within a psychiatric inpatient hospital as a member of the psychiatric team, in an

outpatient clinic as an equal member of the psychotherapy staff, or in community art therapy with various populations and problems. A Studio Art approach invites the client into an artist-like studio to create alongside the art therapist. In recent years, art therapy has expanded its perimeters and shown its usefulness in ever-expanding circles. It seems unlimited in its potential. In a financial climate in which the arts have all but disappeared in public education, ironically, art therapy has become increasingly well known. In this way, diversity can clearly be an advantage within the art therapy community and even thrive with such an image on the outside of the umbrella of identity.

Where diversity can become a disadvantage and a threat to a coherent identity within the art therapy community is when a right/wrong stance is taken. When organized art therapy was established, ideas of art making *within* a psychotherapeutic tradition were central. Eventually, some felt that art and creativity were not emphasized enough from this point of view and refocused on the *art itself* in art therapy. In theory, there is nothing wrong with this shift; in actuality, the pendulum swung so that one approach became good and the other, all too often, bad. Included in the pendulum swing was the belief that the art therapist must consistently and whole-heartedly create art to be effective as a practicing art therapist. (While this idea has become a truism in the field, there is no research that I know of to support it.) Wadeson writes, "I think art therapists get themselves into trouble when they apply 'either/or' definitions. I believe art therapy can embrace many ways of working which need not compete with each other." There is an obvious question here: Why can't diverse ways of working in art therapy all be seen as good?

I have written before that the dialectical positioning of something versus something else is a holdover from a vision of the world as composed of friends and enemies (Junge, 2008). With inclusive and pervasive globalization, this dialectical model, which separates and opposes, has long ago receded as the predominant worldview or paradigm. However, ideas as basic and culturally embedded as this take a long time and much difficulty to change. In my view, the old paradigm of oppositional forces still holds sway in much art therapy thinking.

With such grand diversity, even within the art therapy community, confusion exists about which is the "real" art therapy definition. The professional identity–"the image on the outside of the umbrella," may be the bigger problem. In my opinion, because of its internal diversity and either/or stance, a lack of clarity is common. This leads to the endless questions, "What IS art therapy, anyway?" At this point, the image on art therapy's umbrella presented to the outside world is really *many different images.* The old joke about the blind men touching different parts of the camel and making assumptions about the whole seems an appropriate metaphor. At best, a professional identity of many and differing images is plainly confusing. It is often altogether perplexing and sometimes even totally incoherent. What is different and unique about the tremendously innovative field of art therapy may be inescapably lost. In *Introduction to Art Therapy* (2010), Judith Rubin states,

> In the years since the first edition of this book [1984] was published, an awareness of "art therapy" as an idea has become part of our culture. This heightened consciousness of the healing power of art has also bred confusion. It seems, therefore, even more imperative today to clarify the distinctions between trained art therapists and others providing therapeutic art activities. This list includes artists-in-residence, art teachers and volunteers who provide therapeutic art activities to individuals under stress. . . . This list also includes psychologists, social workers, counselors and psychiatrists who request drawings or incorporate creative tasks in their clinical practice. (p. 26)

A "good/bad" stance prevalent in the art therapy community has been mentioned before. It tends to arise from a spirit of competition that has unfortunately existed in the field since its inception and, in my view, still prevails today. The establishment of the AATA was an example of strong personalities with disparate viewpoints, coming together into the art therapy tent. The founders were predominantly women, and my theory is that they could express their aggressions and fight openly within the art therapy arena when it was likely not safe to do so elsewhere because of the pronounced cultural gender discrimination and misogyny. But rather than an "us against them" stance, what, was provoked was an "us against us" position, which, in large part has come down through the generations and still exists today.

With today's demands and realities, a strong cooperative spirit in art therapy must be achieved and an identity portrayed as a coherent vision on the outside of the umbrella for it to survive and endure. This goal is easier said than done, but suggestions for an Action Plan to get to art therapy cooperation will be presented in the last chapters of this book.

ART THERAPY REGISTRATION, CERTIFICATION, AND PROGRAM ACCREDITATION

Art therapy registration (Art Therapist Registered: ATR) and Certification (Board Certified: BC) are credentials offered by the American art therapy community through the Art Therapy Certification Board (ATCB) representing official recognition that an art therapist has met standards in the case of the ATR and, in addition, has passed an informational test for Board Certification. Standards for the ATR were established soon after its founding by the AATA, while Board Certification is more recent. These initials after an art therapist's name are intended as shorthand to indicate a more experienced art therapist than one who has recently graduated from a master's program. *They establish that the holder has met a series of advanced requirements, but they have nothing to do with state licensing.* This model is not unlike that of other professional organizations for which specific state licensing is spotty or non-existent. Examples are counseling, which offers a Board Certification credential (NBCC), and social work, which provides entrance into its Academy of Certified Social Workers (ACSW). Both certifications are earned by meeting specific requirements set out by the national professional organizations involved.

What do registration and certification have to do with art therapy identity? First, between trying to understand what is required for a state license (which is typically NOT under the name of art therapy) and figuring out the requirements for Registration and Board Certification (which may not be the same as the requirements for licensing), art therapists often become confused and may even give up altogether. If they wish to practice in a state in which there is an appropriate mental health license, it is typically an umbrella license at best, and often what makes art therapists license eligible is not the art therapy part but the "other." It's the words problem again. In order to become license-eligible, art therapists must often portray themselves as something other than art therapists. But if I am then licensed as the "other," am I still an art therapist?

An additional factor is that art therapy Registration and Board Certification are not well recognized in the external, clinical world and often are not known at all. There is little, if any, understanding of its meaning in clinics, institutions, and the mental health world. A medical doctor who is Board Certified is recognized as someone with an advanced credential signifying excellence. The awareness of this model has become well known in many mental health disciplines. Unfortunately, to date, this is generally not so of art therapy. While registered and credentialed art therapists may be justly proud of their achievements, these do not tend to be recognized by the outside world, leading to more explanations and more difficulty with professional identity. I believe increased awareness is a necessity and is a matter of an effective public relations campaign.

To receive the American Art Therapy Association's stamp of "Approval,"[10] an art therapy master's program must demonstrate that it offers a curriculum meeting specific standards. "Approval," like accreditation, is not intended as recognition of excellence or quality but rather an acknowledgment that the program satisfies proscribed curriculum requirements and the program faculty meets certain standards. Again, it is a shorthand: When a graduate of an "Approved" program applies to the ATCB for art therapy Registration/Board Certification, that they attended an "Approved" program signifies that they have satisfied certain basic requirements. A graduate who attended a program *without* AATA Approval can also gain Registration/Board Certification, but they must go through the tedious process of documenting that their educational program met required standards.

The formalization of art therapy education and Registration/Board Certification was created with the goal of replicating a system already in place for other mental health disciplines and therefore gaining professionalism, credibility, and legitimacy for the field. However, some art therapists worried (and still worry) that institutionalization and standardization could likely obliterate intuition and creativity. Writing to Edith Kramer, Myra Levick, the first president of the AATA said,

10. "Approval" is a form of program accreditation granted by the Educational Program Approval Board of the AATA. The process does not require that the program undergo a *site visit,* which could lead to the term "Accreditation" rather than "Approval."

I agree with you; there is much to be said against the acquiring of degrees. Nevertheless, this is the system, and until we can come up with a better one, we have no choice . . . we must start somewhere (cited in Junge, 2010, pp. 185 & 186)

Although the establishment of standards initially promoted necessary goals for the art therapy field, times have changed and there are negatives (which may be more prevalent today) associated with these adaptations of standards. Ilger (1990) states, "credentializing in any field is a defensive strategy"(p. 153). Rogers (1973) writes, "[certification] tends to freeze professions and discourage innovation" (p. 379). Art therapist Arthur Robbins states:

> I accept the development of standards, both for art therapy programs and the certifying process. Yet I am constantly preoccupied by the developing bureaucracy of art therapy, which may be more concerned with regulations than with imparting room and space for creative expression and exploration . . . I fear that the very creative may move to other fields that are not so restrictive. Is it possible, I wonder, to maintain standards and still make room for the experimental and the nonconventional? (cited in Junge & Wadeson, 2006, p. 270)

Has art therapy grown too bureaucratic, too standardized, and too institutionalized? Must art therapy lose its creativity and innovation to be "acceptable"? We are now more than 10 years into the 21st century, and it has been a long time—almost 40 years in some instances—since the AATA established much needed standards for Registration/Board Certification and program approval. Urgently needed is a careful look at where art therapy as a profession is and where it wants to go. It is time to carefully reassess and even change these procedures and standards. Change can lead to the necessary *self*-definition of art therapy identity and its relationship to the external world.

HOW CAN ART THERAPY BE "WELCOMING" AND MAINTAIN AN IDENTITY AS A UNIQUE PROFESSION?

Remembering Rubin's previous statement about the confusion of art therapists with others who use therapeutic art activities, this section focuses on the perspective of the art therapist as consultant and/or teacher to others. Art therapists typically spend a good deal of money and time on their specialized master's education, yet that fact is seldom known or understood by other mental health professionals or by the public at large. They are not simply crayon-toting people who used to be artists. Nevertheless, the client-produced art image intrigues and never ceases to fascinate. If I introduce myself as a psychotherapist or social worker, the person's eyes glaze over, they look away, and they do not pursue other questions. If I introduce myself as an art therapist, interest is ignited, and the desire to know more is evident. I have heard professionals say they were burnt out until the use of the art image reinvigorated them and their practice. There is generally some recognition that art therapists know more than others about art integrated with therapy and even during internships—although they are just learning and may think they don't know what they are doing (and they may be right)—students are often called on to help colleagues understand art produced in a therapy session and/or suggest an appropriate art directive to use with a client or group. In addition, the graduate art therapist may function as a guest facilitator to provide a group experience or workshop with art regularly or periodically for an ongoing group.

A request for help from an art therapist by a colleague is usually viewed positively; the art therapist may be flattered to be asked—and the request may even be seen as a welcome endorsement of the art therapy profession. The art therapist likes to help, after all. But too often, these requests emerge from the idea of the art in therapy as a *technique* and the misunderstanding that *anybody can do it.* Art therapists may find their practices and sometimes their jobs abandoning them in favor of a system that believes that anyone with markers, crayons and a few directives can be an art therapist. The question is an urgent and tricky one that, as far as I know, has never been discussed in art therapy education: How can an art therapist be helpful while not "giving away the store"?

A necessary priority is the consciousness and awareness that each art therapist in the field has an important role to fulfill in whatever she or he does: This is, *teaching about what art therapy* is covertly and overtly. Some mental health disciplines do not carry this teaching function with them. Despite what is overtly going on, always underneath is *the teaching role* that the art therapist embodies, with a need to *clarify and promote the profession.* Whether providing help to colleagues or offering an art therapy group or workshop, the art therapist must work to clear up the considerable confusion about the identity, skills, and values of the professional art therapist and somebody who simply engages in therapeutic art activities. In this role, the individual art therapist and the art therapy student can be aided by the master's educational programs, local art therapy organizations, and the national organizations including the American Art Therapy Association.

Many people—art therapists and others—believe that the making of art and the creation of an art image are always positive. This is simply not true. Fledgling art therapists are often so enthusiastic about the field that they only see the positives. Most consumers (and clients) knowing little about the depths and potentialities of art remain convinced that creativity is always a good thing and creative productions are always positive. Even art therapist Edith Kramer's theory rests heavily on the idea of the psychodynamic defense mechanism "sublimation," in which unacceptable or aggressive impulses are transformed through sublimation in art into something that is then socially acceptable. The theory does not consider the concept that many impulses may remain untransformed and still unacceptable. I remember that in *Teacher,* New Zealand author Sylvia Ashton-Warner (1963) , wrote "[A student] can draw my house in flames," implying that through artwork, the need to actually light her house on fire was gone. We live in a time where clearly this is not so, if it ever was, and mass murders have become all too common an event in our cultural landscape.

Much imagery comes directly from the unconscious, and the experienced and mature art therapist understands that a concrete art image may reveal an uncomfortable, unexpected, and untimely confrontation with a previously secret and unknown inner self. I have written about this problem before. In "Women and Creativity with Two Case Studies of the Artists Frida Kahlo and Diane Arbus," I speculated that Arbus's photographs may have helped cause her suicide and that *if* she could have stopped photographing the subjects she did, she might have been able to stay alive (Junge, 2008.) In a post-master's curriculum I designed, an entire class called "The Dangers of Art Therapy."

There are many ways to handle this paradox. It should be said, it is a struggle and is never easy. But the first necessity—the *sine qua non*—is the *recognition* that this dilemma of possible harm exists underlying all art therapy. Within the art therapy community, frank conversations on the issue could help.

THE ROLE OF ART THERAPY EDUCATIONAL PROGRAMS IN THE DEVELOPMENT OF IDENTITY

Where potential art therapists acquire identity is typically in and during their graduate program, and it takes awhile. They study the values, attitudes, history, theory, and practice of the field in classroom work and during clinical internships. Perhaps most importantly, during these years, they also come in contact with practicing art therapists who make art therapy come alive as a realistic and exciting endeavor. What is taught may not be as important as who teaches it. The process of building identity involves strong relationships with teachers, mentors, and student colleagues. Coppock (2012) states, "It takes time for professional identity to develop, and it takes strong mentors who are willing to invest their time and energy not only in teaching but in leadership and advocacy" (p. 2).

Rightly, most art therapy programs invest time and energy into the evolution of the development of identity. But historically, this has been a rather indirect proposition. My contention is that *now* they must, much more *overtly,* acknowledge the implicit questions of identity, such as "Who are we?" "Who do we want to be?" "What does a graduate need to do to achieve a professional identity?" "Where is the field now?" and "Where should it be going?" Art therapy educational programs must insist that students explicitly, honestly, and realistically grapple with these questions. Perhaps an ongoing identity journal, started on the first day of school and continuing through graduation and beyond, would help focus attention. My speculation is that the issue of their art therapy identity has not been a matter that many art therapists have realistically come to grips with; in any case, serious reassessment and planning is a necessity in the challenging cultural and mental health milieu of today. Underlying this essential endeavor is the notion that program teaching faculty must struggle with and define both personal and professional identity as a member of the art therapy community. Students get their identity messages from program leaders, teachers, and mentors, but this can be a much more complex issue in dual-degree programs and should not be ignored.

In a questionnaire, I asked beginning art therapy students and recent graduates to rate the strength of their identity. As to be expected, art therapy master's students tend to begin a program with some self-identified personal identity and little or no professional identity. Also to be expected, new graduates consistently describe themselves as having stronger identities than when they began, but confusion is also often part of the deal–particularly in dual-degree programs. One recent grad who described both personal and professional identity as "Medium" wrote, "I still struggle to hone my identity as an art therapist and often find myself unsure if to tell people I am a therapist, an art therapist . . . or an intern. . . . It is not only confusing in conversation, I feel it reflects my own inner confusion" (Junge, 2012a, 2012b.) Within a graduate program, the student feels a protective connection to cohorts, professors, and mentors, and identity grows. What happens after graduation when the departure from the protective environment ends, is the bigger problem.

LONELINESS OF THE LONG-DISTANCE ART THERAPY GRADUATE

Today, the art therapy master's graduate, burdened with huge amounts of student loans, may exit into a world where finding employment, if possible, is not easy, where a living wage is hard to achieve, and where art therapy education and practice may not be understood. To earn art therapy registration, supervision of clinical work is required–often for about 2 years. To earn a state license, supervision of clinical work is required–often for about 2 years. These supervision experiences cost money the graduate may not have; the art therapy graduate may even need two (paid) supervisors to meet the specified requirements for licensing and registration. The novice art therapist may decide it is necessary to pursue supervision with a non-art therapist, and therefore post-master's mentorship and role modeling by an art therapist are lost. These are some realities of the real world, and idealistic graduate art therapists may suffer a significant sense of disappointment in their chosen field. While graduation is often called "commencement," it is seldom thought of as that, and graduation/commencement is a critical identity point.

Long ago, family therapist Carl Whitaker advocated a post-graduate "Cuddle Group" for therapists. Intended as a learning/supervision experience, its title also speaks to a *nurturing function*–as an extension of the protected academic environment. In the outside world, the art therapist may feel quite alone and actually, may be the *only one* in a clinic staff of mental health professionals. A "Cuddle Group" can provide an ongoing learning experience where art therapy colleagues regularly get together as they move forward with an intellectual goal of sorting out clinical work and also to struggle with the particular challenges of being an art therapist today and with living the profession.

For an art therapist, a "Cuddle Group" can provide necessary nurturing and ease the sense of being alone. Professional identity develops and may strengthen or diminish in the years after formal education. My guess is that if art therapy educational programs, as a matter of course, offered free groups to their graduates, what might be the *professional developmental stage* of loneliness and disappointment could be eased and the evolution of a growing, even flourishing, art therapy identity enhanced. It is not that the art therapist's identity is so fragile as to immediately fall away. But in our culture today, as budgets tighten, the arts in education have all but disappeared, and therapies, except for forms of behaviorism, are being questioned and even abandoned; there are few supportive resources for the practicing art therapist and few clinics willing to invest in developing staff and skills. Loneliness can be a significant and usually ignored factor. In my opinion, a group such as this would not only be a gift to the participants but a major benefit to the profession.

Chapter 4

ESSAYS ON IDENTITY BY ART THERAPISTS

ARTIST IN RESIDENCE IN THE STUDIO OF THE SOUL: A QUEST FOR AN IDENTITY

Pat B. Allen, PhD, ATR, HLM

We are called throughout our existence to encounter challenges, play different roles in relation to others, and sort through the gifts and obstacles conferred by our family, the zeitgeist, and the particular body and soul we brought into this lifetime. Consciously or not, the sum of our response to these experiences eventually constitutes our identity. If we are fortunate, our identity mirrors our true self: We can listen for what calls us, and we can follow what inspires us with passion. If we have suffered early loss, trauma, or neglect, we may be more focused on what supports survival and mitigates anxiety, and the music of desire may be faint and far off. I came to art therapy as an early identity for reasons of personal inadequacy. Although I was attracted to art, I lacked sufficient ego strength to be an artist. I had a largely unconscious need to help others that arose from early responsibility of having to care for a sick mother who died when I was a teenager. Fear of death drove me to seek a career identity quickly. I didn't feel I had the luxury to fool around trying out different paths. My fundamental conflicts prevented me from deciding on a course that seemed to place my desires before the needs of others.

Art therapy on its surface provides a great solution: Art is present, and one's conscience can relax because others are being served. I have continued to work out these issues of right relationship to self and others, the nature of service, the meaning of creativity, and the place of pleasure in life. I have described the particulars of my journey with more grace and detail in my books *Art Is a Way of Knowing* (1995) and *Art Is a Spiritual Path* (2005).

I am not sure whether art therapists will find an echo of similar conflicts buried under the rosy rhetoric of the profession. Perhaps I am alone in wincing at the cheery stories often told of how the art therapist "always loved stories and pictures" or how the field is such a marvelous hybrid of art and therapy. In studying nature, I have learned that hybridity is not an unalloyed good. A hybrid plant is created to emphasize a particular trait or quality, but its reproduction often yields weaker even sterile versions of the original. I sometimes wonder whether this is the fate of art therapy. For the purpose of this essay I decided to share my remembrances of a series of therapeutic relationships that each helped form my identity in relation to art therapy.

When I scheduled a chat to ask what he knew about art therapy as a possible career, the counselor at the Boston Museum School of Fine Arts where I was an undergrad suggested I explore some therapy for myself. I may have seemed shocked–the notion that I might need help was completely foreign to me. Perhaps in deference to my reaction, he suggested the relative anonymity of the counseling center at Tufts University, where Museum School degree students took our academic classes. I had no knowledge of psychology at the time nor any model for considering the effects of life events on my inability to focus and engage fully in my coursework. Art therapy had already come into my awareness and seemed like a viable solution to resolve my inability to dive deeply into art making and the nagging concern that art was a frivolous waste of time while there is suffering in the world. That I might not be entirely responsible for that suffering never occurred to me.

It was a long ride on public transportation to get to Tufts and a long walk across campus, where I marveled at the seemingly normal, motivated, and goal-directed students milling about who seemed as like me as space aliens. At the counseling center, I must have had an intake, must have said something to get started. What I remember is that I sat in a chair and cried silently hour after hour, week after week, while the therapist focused her eyes on the middle distance, quietly giving me space for whatever it was that was going on inside me to at last leak out in the presence of another human being. Each week, exhausted, I rode back to the dingy basement apartment with bars on the windows where I lived alone. The endeavor seemed futile, but I kept going back.

Eventually, I began to draw pictures and bring them to therapy. I began to do this, I think, when I finally started talking and found my efforts to communicate my feelings in words weren't working. I recall telling the therapist that I felt as if I was removing rotted plasterboard from a wall in a house, only to find swarming insects underneath. She suggested that perhaps therapy could help brush away the insects and replace the plasterboard. I found this framing of the image so blatantly terrible that I decided she must be an idiot. In reflecting later, I realized that in my mind's eye, behind the plasterboard, beneath the swarming insects, was hidden a beautifully carved balustrade. I never told her my version of the metaphor nor that I had been as enormously reassured and comforted by it as I had been appalled and insulted by her interpretation. It was not an image that I purposefully imagined to make myself feel better but rather something that appeared unbidden and with a life of its own.

I have scant memory of the mercifully little the therapist said in our sessions. But I have no doubt that it was her ability to simply sit in witness to my state of being, my silence and anguish without demanding that I talk, without asking questions or trying to make me feel better that was the valuable part of what she did. I was far from the place of needing to make sense of my feelings since this was the first I knew of their existence and simply feeling was overwhelming. I felt within an endless well of sadness, not tethered to words, to experiences, or to life events but more like a rushing darkness, a bleak damp wind that cut to the bone. I made crude sketches to illustrate a sense of my internal landscape. In one I drew broken bottles inside me whose sharp edges threatened to cut me if I moved too much. The mind was refuge, the body treacherous. Therapy was somehow breaking these bottles, but it was a risky proposition: I could bleed to death. I did not need her to understand; I simply needed her to be in the room. In fact I couldn't tolerate any expression of empathy at all. I could barely tolerate her presence.

Also, I hated her. Ms. Curtin was a blonde, middle-aged psychologist. Utterly ordinary, kind, able at least to withstand week after week of silent sad rage occupying the chair opposite her. I hated her irrationally; I hated her with red-hot silent venom that welled up in me like poison. We call that transference, and it is a horrible feeling when one has sufficient wits to recognize that this person has done nothing to deserve this rancor. The discrepancy between this composed, neutral-seeming person and sweaty, angry, and worst-of-all crying mess of me was all but unbearable. I found my way to drawing the pain out of frustration with my inability to put anything into words without crying. Words had always been my strong suit. I was smart and verbal, often cutting and sarcastic. I was not sentimental or emotional. I hated her because I was unable to speak easily and without emotion about pain that some part of me had decided to view with contempt and rejection. For those 50 minutes each week, I could get a glimpse of the broken rage I carried inside by projecting it onto another person. During those minutes, space was being made within me while those feelings vacated or at least went to their own corner of the boxing ring. Gradually rage subsided and sadness could show up. Toward the end of our work together, I gave Ms. Curtin a pen and ink drawing titled "Therapy." It depicted a dragon sitting in a chair holding up a mask of a depressed face opposite a therapist looking quite like her holding up a mask that was identical to the face underneath. She had succeeded in helping me begin to master the worst of myself, the monstrousness of a teenager who wished her sick mother would die already and all the other guilt entwined with duty, misshapen care enfolded in self-abnegation that occupied my inner life and prevented a healthy identity from taking root. All this was felt but not spoken.

My second significant therapy relationship was with Margaret Naumburg, pioneer art therapist, and it took place partly at the same time as the relationship with Ms. Curtin. Margaret was unhappily retired in Boston, in her 80s when I met her. As she did with at least one other young student, who happened to be my best friend, she took me on in an undefined relationship that included assisting her with her writing, taking her shopping, as well as directing me in her version of art therapy. I was appreciative of Margaret's direction of how to paint to get at unconscious content. She had me soak large watercolor paper in the bathtub, use large brushes, and paint from dreams. Scribble drawings and spontaneous drawings became my regular practice, along with writing in a loose-leaf notebook any thoughts and associations that came up. Again, this work and its significance are explored in more detail in *Art Is a Way of Knowing*. What is pertinent here for my still-forming identity are intertwined events that, in a way quite different from my experience of therapy with Ms. Curtin, also center on transference.

I had discovered art therapy through reading Naumburg's books in the library at some point in my art school experience before meeting her. I was quite excited about the idea, as it seemed to solve my dilemma of discomfort with being an artist and a dire need to be of service. It offered an identity. When I learned that Margaret was in Boston, I felt sure this was a sign of my future direction. When I met Naumburg, she assured me that art therapy was indeed my path. I discussed all this in therapy as well, but when I began to describe painting from dreams and bringing them to Naumburg, Ms. Curtin suggested that the work seemed to be therapy and that working with more than one therapist was probably not a good idea. I shared this concern with Naumburg. She responded by saying the therapist was probably just intimidated by her fame. In fact, Ms. Curtin had never heard of Naumburg or her work until I brought it to her attention. Yet I threw my lot in with Margaret and quit therapy. I had gotten a job in a mental health center, and the identity of art therapist was beginning to take hold.

The effect of this decision was to allow the next phase of transference to emerge full blown. I began to dread calling Margaret or going to see her. We had been meeting weekly so that we could discuss a new book she was writing, which I was typing for her. After ignoring her calls for a week or more, she finally confronted me about what was going on. I said I was feeling terribly resistant to seeing her and was worried about her health. She laughed on the phone and assured me it was simply mother transference and I should come right over. I felt a weight lift. In fact I had a recurring fantasy that I was at her door in Longwood Towers, and she did not answer my knock because she was dead on the floor in her apartment. When I got to her place, we settled down to talk, and I shared my concerns more graphically. She simply got up and moved to the other end of the couch and changed the subject. "Shall we get to work on the book?" was her reply.

My transference contained the unconscious wish for death of a figure of oppression. I had come to resent typing Margaret's manuscript, which seemed like a vague mish mash of her prior works. I also felt a compulsion to protect her from becoming aware of what I saw as her waning powers, so I would edit and rewrite her words. She was delighted with the result while not acknowledging that I was doing so. These actions echoed sufficiently my relationship with my own mother, whom I resented as her needs for care overtook my adolescent desire to go out with friends and do whatever I chose. Yet my mother was blameless and suffering from cancer; anger toward her would have been unthinkable. Our family also shared the belief that it would be harmful to let my mother know how ill she really was. I resented carrying the burden of knowledge of my mother's impending death while with Naumburg I resented writing her book for her. It was with relief that I returned to therapy with Ms. Curtin when Naumburg decided, with no further discussion of transference, or indeed of countertransference, that she could no longer mentor me.

By the time of my next significant therapy relationship, I had fully embraced my career and identity as an art therapist. I had earned a master's degree in art therapy and was teaching in an art therapy training program, working on both psychiatric and addiction units of an inpatient facility, and carrying out a small private practice. I was also married and contemplating starting a family. I was growing more and more uncomfortable with the interpretive aspect of art therapy. What I was *not* doing was making art myself. I was fully into burnout mode. The prominence of the caretaking aspects of art therapy had frozen my own creative impulse. While art therapists often cite a lack of time as a reason that they stop making art, I suspect there are other more salient reasons. Initially, the intimacy of the therapeutic relationship and the enjoyment of providing the art making experience to others can feel sustaining. We experience an as-if pleasure via the art created by our patients. But few workplaces are set up to support or nurture the creativity of employees. Without peers engaged in creative work, art therapists may drift into the language and practices of the majority of their clinical colleagues. The craft of identity becomes remade into something seemingly more serviceable, as service dominates the identity equation and art recedes (Allen, 1992).

I considered that further training might help rejuvenate me, and I sought Jungian analytic training. I'd been interested in Jung since graduate school but had found little resonance for his ideas in art therapy. I was gently informed that before being considered for training, I must undergo a thorough training analysis. I was referred to a woman analyst who quickly identified my predicament in Jungian terms: an overdeveloped thinking function, a somewhat atrophied intuitive function, a recently accessed but undeveloped feeling function, and an all but dormant sensation function. After hearing my story and noting that the loss of my mother was the central theme of my narrative, she sent me home with the task to listen to Leonard Bernstein's recording of the *Kaddish,* the Jewish prayer for the dead. She suggested that music is a powerful tool for accessing both feeling and sensation. As I played this recording over and over, the floodgates opened, by magic it seemed to me. My grudging tears shed in the painful sessions with my first therapist broke the dam that began to give me access to feelings. Bernstein's music and the ancient words of the prayer not only opened me but connected me to a profound tradition of understanding and honoring grief that changed my life. Death is never mentioned in the Mourner's Kaddish. Rather, it is a prayer of praise and blessing of the Divine. Still, the sound and cadence of the ancient words penetrated me and fed my soul. I was not alone in being marked by grief. Others had also suffered and still found their way to meaning and a belief in something larger than themselves.

When my analyst moved from the area, she referred me to another Jungian, a man this time; images flowed, and I reclaimed piece after piece of myself. Eventually an image emerged that made it clear to both of us that I was being called on a mythic journey via the image. A large green dragon telling a story to a tiny child seated on its lap emerged in a pastel drawing. This image contained the next challenge of identity. Perhaps because the analyst was a man, perhaps because I was more experienced in following the image and trusting it, or simply because I had healed and matured sufficiently, the image of the dragon and the child spoke eloquently to me and to my analyst about the current state of the transference. The dragon was the same character that had appeared in my drawing for my first therapist. Perhaps everything I had considered to be monstrous somehow had the power to nurture a nascent creative identity. I began to do active imagination with the image at home. I settled myself into a relaxed state and allowed the image to unfold to its next iteration and made a quick sketch in pencil. I felt drawn to using oil paints on canvas, which I primed and stretched myself. When the first painting was finished, I repeated the process of active imagination and sketching and ultimately completed seven 15″ x 18″ oil paintings over many months.

When I brought each image to my sessions, the analyst and I simply looked at them wordlessly. I learned through this shared gaze the power of silent witness to sustain the creative process. The story contained in those seven images did not initially yield its meaning to my attempts to write it down. I framed the paintings, hung them in my home, and lived with them. Their presence in my field over time instructed me, entered me, and changed me. I learned it is by holding truth that the image heals me. Interpretation stops the story within the limitations of present understanding.

The identity I have grown to trust and embrace is that of the *conscious artist in residence.* Deborah Gadiel, my student and former colleague, used this term in her master's thesis, and I found it worked to describe what I was aiming for. The elaboration of this identity as an alternative to that of art therapist has been refined and developed through more than 20 years of practice by myself and others at the Open Studio Project. The artist in residence holds the space by embodying truth and authenticity in her own artistic process in the presence of others. She sees to the order of the studio, the fitness of tools and materials. She must cultivate a disciplined compassionate disinterest in the psychological processes of the others present and the recognition that each artist is doing a piece of the work that is larger than all of us. This requirement is in direct opposition to the concerns of a therapist.

The artist in residence as a role of service in the studio is primarily mundane and simple: keep the place clean and orderly, and ring a chime to let everyone know how much time is left in a studio session. Ensure the few rules are scrupulously followed: Each one present is responsible to set his or her own intention, no comments about art work are allowed, careful silent witness but no interference in the process of others is required, respect for the relationship of the maker to the image is paramount. These rules allow for a sacred space to exist that supports the spiritual journey toward Self that Carl Jung describes as individuation. I intuit another aspect of the conscious artist in residence identity that I cannot prove. As we seek to make known all parts of our self, dark and light, exalted and stumbling, joyous, jealous, frightened, and fearless, we may be calling forth these attributes not only in each other but in the Source itself. Perhaps what we paint and come to know we also call into being in the world. If we are able to see all this with eyes of compassion toward each other and toward ourselves, we may be making a new reality in which living together in peace is more than a dream.

References

Allen, P. (1992). Artist in residence: An alternative to clinification for the art thera-
pist. *Art Therapy: Journal of the American Art Therapy Association, 9*(1), 22–29.
Allen, P. (1995). *Art is a way of knowing.* Boston: Shambhala Publications.
Allen, P. (2005). *Art is a spiritual path.* Boston: Shambhala Publications.

MY IDENTITY: A MOSAIC DESIGN

Charlotte Boston, MA, ATR-BC

A mosaic is defined as art consisting of a design made of small pieces of colored stone or glass. As an art therapist, I have a "mosaic" of roles, each of which is a part that contributes to the whole image and design of who I am. I am an artist, therapist, clinician, facilitator, educator, and nurturer. I feel as if I am also a minister as I am witness to what is often a sacred creative space and process to watch as my patients make artwork. I am a woman from a rich heritage of people who have survived tremendous odds in the midst of few resources and challenging life experiences. I often feel as if I am a translator too. This is defined by my responsibility to report on and document artwork from patients in understandable terms for non-art therapy, multidisciplinary staff, which includes but is not limited to social workers, interns, nurses, psychiatric technicians, psychiatrists, and various expressive therapy staff.

The most important elements of my personal identity are the knowledge, skills, and abilities gained from my culture, being an artist and a therapist. As I began in art therapy, much of my work and motivation was to contribute to improved cultural sensitivity and competency to better meet the needs of minority populations who are serviced by art therapists. The artist in me is happiest creating for hours, whether it is with semiprecious stones, oil pastels, ceramics, watercolors, collage— and the list goes on. To create feels nearly as natural as breathing. The therapeutic element of my identity has proven to be useful and broadly enlightening as a professional in my roles as clinician, therapist, clinician, and educator.

In many metropolitan areas, the climate of inpatient psychotherapy is short term with a high population of diverse cultures. When I consider my heritage, my gender, my life experiences, and the populations most served by mental health agencies where I live, I think I have a unique advantage in being able to empathize with this population to facilitate therapy. I have been in the field of art therapy for more than 25 years, and in that time, my identity has changed. Because of the varied experiences of my work with different populations, my identity has been enhanced and expanded. I notice my perceptions of culture broadening as I reflect the diversity of the population shift in the United States over the past 12 to 15 years.

Most of the years of my work as an art therapist have been in a psychiatric inpatient setting in a metropolitan area. The current staff is as multicultural as the populations we serve, so much so that the hospital has had a language telephone line established, which can translate in 67 languages. Many patients are Spanish speaking. A few speak Farsi or Ebo. We have patients and staff from French-speaking African countries and some who are deaf. In this setting, services provided are predominantly art as therapy. This has changed from a few years ago when more groups were insight-oriented art psychotherapy groups. A series of changes in management, budget, and programming shifted. At my facility, I provide four art therapy groups per day and document each. The size of patient groups often ranges from 9 to 20 and is usually held in an open common area of the patient unit. Groups typically include a mixture of patients with a broad range of diagnoses, some of whom are concretely oriented and some who are able to abstract information.

Historically, most inpatient psychiatric hospitals in the United States operate from a medical model, which is sometimes perceived as Western, scientifically oriented, and focused. In these facilities, art therapy has usually not been understood as scientific as "medicine" but is often considered an *alternative* therapy similar to Eastern methods of healing such as yoga, acupuncture, or Tai Chi.

My art therapy identity does not always fit with my employment. There have been times when the clinical and business sides of my work clash, and this impacts what I do. The business budgetary leaders want art therapists to provide as many groups as possible in the course of a day. They do not consider time to process the group with patients, document the group in the patient charts, and give barely enough time to restore and maintain materials between groups. Another example relates to the current budget for my department: We order small quantities of basic art materials regularly so that we don't run out. Specialty items are ordered as needed, but due to budget limitations, these are minimal. The type and variety of art materials and sometimes the quality of materials limited. Even being resourceful, there have been times when we had to use half sheets of paper or change the art task for group because we didn't have enough materials for the large number of groups we have to run in the course of a day. Currently, I also conduct a few non-art therapy groups, which are usually "skills based." These groups may focus on social skills, grief and loss, or relaxation techniques. This form of group is an effort to reduce expenses, maintain our work hours, and meet some remaining needs of patients. In other words, the art therapist is asked to provide a group where one does not need to use art materials or does so minimally.

There is a good deal of pressure having to run four to five groups per day; I often feel rushed and don't have enough time to process the groups with patients or plan for follow up themes/projects. It's my opinion that mental health in general puts the emphasis on the quantity of groups over the quality of groups, and this quantity emphasis causes me sometimes to not do art therapy. I'm sure this is impacted by decreasing patient stays, fewer admissions, and significantly reduced Medicaid/Medicare reimbursement in psychiatric hospitals. It is increasingly difficult to work in the mental health system these days. This change impacts my identity as an art therapist as I consider how I can use my art therapy skills more fully–whether I need to explore other possibilities for work, earn an additional degree, or expand one of the elements most important to me for employment.

While I am gratified by the work I am able to do with my patients, I am most gratified by my part-time work outside of my main job as an on-campus supervisor for graduate art therapy students at the university and by my activity on the board of the AATA. I am revived by this work because my knowledge and skills are put to good use–especially training art therapy graduate students. In my work in AATA, I feel that I have a behind-the-scenes view of the concerns of members and am making an impact to advocate for the profession and interact with art therapists nationally.

When I think of the many ways art therapy is used as well as the broad diversity of art therapists and populations, I do not think the field would benefit right now from a unitary identity. A unitary identity seems to imply that there *is only one way* to be an art therapist, only one way to create art and only one way to facilitate art therapy when there are many ways. However, a unitary identity in art therapy may have positive aspects as it could provide the field with more credibility, respect, and/or recognition among local and state legislators, insurance companies, as a protected title (used only by trained, credential art therapists) and as a reimbursable profession. Art therapy may certainly benefit from a more unitary identity when it comes to research and assessment methods if this provides art therapy with recognition equivalent to other clinical professionals who have published research, grants, and sponsors. (While the art therapy field has many assessment methods, it still does not have enough published research for each. This seems to be changing.)

In that art and the arts are positive for most people, a unitary identity for art therapy may impact health care in general in ways that can save money and, through preventive care, enhance mastery, lower stress without harmful side effects, and increase self-esteem. Art therapy can improve the quality of life.

Do art therapists need to be practicing artists? I believe as art therapists, we have to be *a product of the product.* Would we want a doctor to perform surgery without training? Some part of us has to be an artist to understand the creative process. We emphasize to art therapy students we teach that they must create in the course of their study. It's expected in many art therapy training programs. Before most of us are accepted into an art therapy program, we must present a portfolio of artwork and meet certain art prerequisites.

It is important that we gain knowledge of the tools we have in order to prescribe their use to clients. I could not competently recommend the appropriate task or media if I didn't have a deep sense of the creative process. It is most beneficial for an art therapist to be an artist. If I were a surgeon, there are many tools and procedures in the field that I would need to become skilled. I couldn't be a surgeon without the knowledge, skills, familiarity, and mastery of the tools of my trade. I believe the same is true for art therapist. My role involves aspects of both art and therapy—using art to heal. How can we know ourselves in the profession without the art?

As a practicing art therapist of 26 years, in a metropolitan area, from an economic point of view, I believe art therapy should be predominantly a mental health discipline. In my area, many art therapists are employed in mental health agencies. In addition, the coursework and supervision in our art therapy graduate programs are preparing and equipping students for licensing exams upon graduation. Licensing is a state requirement, and licensing issues may vary in different areas of the country. When I consider the literature and presentations on art therapy and neuroscience, especially with veterans and trauma work, I believe art therapy is also rehabilitative and educational, although it is not as predominantly recognized as such and varies depending on the setting.

The AATA is art therapy's predominant professional organization. Historically, it has provided a place for art therapists to focus and communicate. It has also created standards for the profession, which have helped the field develop. Depending on leadership, the nature of art therapy identity tends to be defined by AATA, and it has continuing work to do there.

FACILITATING ART THERAPIST PROFESSIONAL IDENTITY THROUGH ART THERAPY EDUCATION

Sarah P. Deaver, PhD, ATR-BC

Fifteen years ago, the American Art Therapy Association[1] made a choice to make art therapists more eligible for state licensing by including counseling courses in art therapy curriculum and standards. The intent of the change was a pragmatic one, which intended to adjust curriculum standards so that art therapy graduates would be eligible for state licensure as professional counselors, thus opening the door for art therapists to be paid at the same level as other master's-level clinicians. The change in educational standards has had a number of ramifications in art therapy education, and this dual-degree idea vastly complicates the creation of an *art therapist* identity.

Some programs struggled to meet counseling board requirements by adding courses to already packed curricula. However, because the art therapy program faculty at Eastern Virginia Medical School (EVMS) had the foresight early on to align our courses with our state counseling board's requirements, since the early 1990s, our graduates have successfully obtained licensure as professional counselors. This seems to have had positive results in terms of employment opportunities and salaries of our graduates. However, four years ago, the name of our program was changed from the "Graduate Art Therapy Program" to "Graduate Art Therapy *and Counseling* Program." Like the AATA curriculum change initiative, this program name change was a pragmatic choice made to ensure that there would be no questions from the Virginia counseling board about whether our graduates were really counselors. Although I understand the logic of the decision, our graduates are not really counselors. They are something more: Art therapists and the "*and Counseling*" in our program name complicates their successful identity formation as *art therapists*. AATA's (2012) current policy regarding licensure seems to focus on an *art therapy license:*

> The American Art Therapy Association supports federal and state policies, legislation, regulations, judicial actions, and initiatives that encour-

---

1. Sarah P. Deaver is the current president of American Art Therapy Association.

age, promote, and support efforts to gain a professional art therapy license and licensure of art therapists.

Until our Virginia state AATA chapter successfully establishes a freestanding art therapy license that is accepted by insurance company provider panels, our graduates continue to pursue licensure as counselors, and my program strives to establish strong art therapist professional identity within our students despite our program's name, which suggests otherwise. Various approaches, curricular and otherwise, enable us to succeed at this program goal.

Curricular and Extracurricular Art-Based Learning

Artistic and psychological inquiry, which result in knowledge of self and other, as well as the inherent aspects of the art process from which this knowledge emerges, are considered to be ways of knowing essential to all facets of scholarly and clinical education in art therapy. (Gerber, 2006, p. 110)

In congruence with Gerber's assertion, at EVMS, we believe in an ethical and professional imperative for art therapists to engage in regular reflective art practice; thus, our program integrates art-based experiential learning into nearly every course, and faculty members and supervisors additionally encourage student art making in response to their internship and non-academic experiences. There is a strong case, both theory and research based, for our doing so.

In terms of theory, student art making may be conceptualized as a constructivist and experiential learning tool. The underlying tenet of constructivism is that new knowledge emerges when individuals compare their current experiences to preexisting assumptions and past experiences (Andresen, Boud, & Cohen, 2000). A constructivist teacher acknowledges and appreciates the different worldviews and perspectives that all learners bring to the classroom and recognizes that students are the makers of their own knowledge (McAuliffe, 2000). These tenets of constructivism are realized through the implementation of art-based experiential activities throughout the graduate curriculum. Students bring their unique personal histories to educational and internship experiences and respond to them through engagement in focused, reflective art making. Engagement in these sorts of art experiences, which may be considered experiential learning (Kolb, 1984), facilitates insight, reflection, and the development of new knowledge (Deaver & McAuliffe, 2009). In this sort of art-based learning, the hands-on process of art making and the brain-based process of gaining meaning and insight from imagery are linked. Arnheim (1980), and Marshall (2007), asserted that art making "allows information to be seen differently, in a fresh, more meaningful, personal, and experiential way (as in art, symbolism, and metaphor). This transformation of concepts through imaging produces new insights and learning" (p. 23). However, Sullivan (2006) and Walker (2004) suggest that art making alone may not be sufficient for meaning making; the act of critical reflection is required in art making in order for art practice to be an opportunity for construction of meaning. Consequently, at EVMS, we attempt to always combine art making with subsequent reflection through responsive writing or class discussion.

Recent research supports the use of art-based learning to attain art therapy educational goals, including the development of art therapist professional identity (Deaver, 2012; Deaver, Elkis-Abuhoff, & Hartzell, 2012; Orkibi, 2010). In a mixed methods study, Elkis-Abuhoff, Gaydos, Rose and Goldblatt (2010) measured art therapy students' professional identity development over several months during the students' internships. Students' drawings that depicted aspects of therapeutic relationships with internship clients were congruent with the results of quantitative measures, which included a statistically significant increase in professional identity development. All student art making built into the EVMS curriculum is aimed at increasing student self-awareness, exploring personal responses to didactic material, and facilitating professional identity through consolidating self-knowledge, art therapy academic content, and emergent clinical skills and experience.

Context for Student Art Making

At EVMS, we engage each cohort of incoming students in a week-long orientation involving learning about each other through sharing and making art, and we introduce students to visual journaling. We encourage students to maintain these journals throughout their two years of graduate school. Visual journaling is particularly valuable to students when they embark on their internships beginning in the second semester of study. Once the academic year begins, in addition to classroom art experiences, we also have a large, fully equipped studio to which the students have access 24 hours a day, seven days a week. Finally, because our studio-based "Art Therapy Processes and Materials" course is only offered in the first year of study, a faculty member facilitates an open studio experience for second-year students one afternoon each week.

Program Design and Curricular Support

Various opportunities for professional identity development are built into the program design. Here are some of them:

- EVMS pays for students' AATA memberships; thus, they receive the informative monthly updates and newsletters, including announcements of chapter events, notices of job openings, and discounts on conference attendance. They may join blogs and discussion groups, networking and interacting with professional art therapists and fellow students. Several have taken advantage of the association's mentorship program and have benefitted from being mentees of professional art therapists outside of the EVMS faculty.
- *Art Therapy: Journal of the American Art Therapy Association* and other art therapy scholarly publications are a major resource for our students. These are readily available through our library, and we update syllabi annually to reflect the most current references and advances in the field.
- The curriculum includes two semesters of "Clinical Case Conference," in which students learn presentation skills and present professional-level case material before an audience of peers.
- At each of three internships, the student is required to present an in-service talk about the profession and aspects of art therapy applicable to the internship site.
- The "Ethics and Professionalism" course includes preparation for employment, such as exposure to local art therapists who describe their career paths on a continuum of practice from inpatient psychiatric settings to open studio work, learning how to develop a professional resume, a mock interview that is filmed and self-critiqued, as well as intense study of the dimensions of practice for art therapists as seen in the AATA ethical principles.

- Three core courses assign differing end-of-semester art works that require students' reflection on their development as emerging professional art therapists. The "Processes and Materials in Art Therapy" course has as its final assignment the creation of an art piece that embodies the student's sense of self as an artist-therapist. The "Symbolism" course requires a piece that embodies the student's explorations and reflections on her own symbolism and imagery as seen in two years of art making, collected imagery and artifacts, and visual journaling. The "Ethics and Professionalism" course's final assignment entails students creating pieces that reflect their emerging identities as ethical professional art therapy practitioners.

The Role of Faculty

As mentors, supervisors, and role models, faculty members play a crucial role in student professional identity development. According to Rønnestad and Skovholt (2003), "the dependency and vulnerability of students make them particularly appreciative of the support and encouragement of more advanced members of the profession"(p. 12). As students progress through the graduate program, they seek out models to emulate (Dulicai, Hays, & Nolan, 1989; Rønnestad & Skovholt, 2003.) EVMS faculty members strive to be professional role models not only through their teaching and supervision but through being actively involved in medical school committees and in our professional association, attending and presenting at the AATA annual conference and other conferences, presenting there with students, and co-authoring papers with students and recent graduates.

Another opportunity for role modeling and support of student professional identity development is through advisement and professional performance reviews. The purpose of these reviews is to monitor students' non-academic and non-clinical performance; in other words, we are monitoring their professional development, including areas such as time management, integrity, interpersonal relationships with peers and faculty, openness to learning, conflict resolution, and self-care. Each student is assigned a faculty advisor, and individual meetings are held at least once each semester. This system establishes a mentor-mentee relationship and provides a venue for students to sort through the challenges and complexities of the graduate school experience.

Threats to Art Therapist Professional Identity

Despite our best efforts and similar efforts made by other art therapy master's programs, there is attrition from the field. Many of our graduates are no longer practicing art therapists. We may attribute this to several factors: Despite high-quality art therapy master's-level education programs from which hundreds of students graduate annually, art therapy job openings continue to be few and far between. New graduates who take a job that is not specifically that of an "art therapist" are perhaps vulnerable to Allen's (1992) "clinification syndrome," in which they drop their commitment to their own art process and get swept up into various other identities such as "counselor." Their identity as art therapists is likely to become lost in the much larger counseling or marriage and family therapy professions.

Many graduates of the EVMS program are faced with practical financial choices, and opt to maintain their counseling license and Art Therapy Credentialing Board (ATCB) credentials rather than join and maintain membership in the AATA—the professional organization—or the state chapter. The resulting lack of affiliation with other art therapists and inability to keep up with current trends in public policy, literature, research, and other professional activity available through membership in a professional organization constitutes a substantial threat to art therapist professional identity. Thus, whereas there is apparent economic value in licensure as counselors or marriage and family therapists, if one is unable to afford membership in one's own professional art therapy association, this is often a substantial problem for the adequate retention and growth of art therapy identity. Groups not associated with the AATA that do not require any membership fee, appeal to recent graduates. However, they may be a threat to a strong, ethical art therapist professional identity because these groups have open membership that includes non-art therapists who use art therapy techniques despite their lacking the requisite education or supervision.

Possible Solutions for Educators

From an education perspective, emphasis needs to be placed on encouraging students' self-awareness, capacity for reflection, and professional identity through in-depth involvement in their own art process. A three-credit "Ethics and Professionalism" course in the final year of study is another successful strategy for students to learn real-life career skills and for exploration of their emerging identities as professional art therapists.

Membership in the AATA significantly enhances art therapist professional identity through affiliation, education, networking, scholarship, and values held in common by its members. Therefore, it makes sense for educators to introduce students to the benefits of membership in their professional association through paying their membership fees. This relatively small cost may have long-term benefits for the field: increased association membership, greater involvement of members in moving the field forward, and stronger individual and collective professional identity.

References

Allen, P. (1992). Artist-in-residence: An alternative to "clinification" for art therapists. *Art Therapy: Journal of the American Art Therapy Association, 9*(1), 22–29.

American Art Therapy Association. (2012). *Position statement on state licensure for art therapists.* Available at http://www.americanarttherapyassociation.org/upload /2012policystatementstatelicensure.pdf

Andresen, L., Boud, D., & Cohen, R. (2000). Experienced-based learning. In G. Foley (Ed.), *Understanding adult education and training* (2nd ed.). Sydney: Allen & Unwin.

Arnheim, A. (1980). A plea for visual thinking. *Critical Inquiry, 6*(3), 489–497.

Deaver, S. (2012). Art-based learning strategies in art therapy graduate education. *Art Therapy: Journal of The American Art Therapy Association, 29*(4), 158–165.

Deaver, S., Elkis-Abuhoff, D., & Hartzell, E. (2012, July). *The role of student art making in art therapy graduate education.* Panel presented at the meeting of the American Art Therapy Association, Savannah, GA.

Deaver, S., & McAuliffe, G. (2009). Reflective visual journaling during art therapy and counseling internships: A qualitative study. *Reflective Practice, 10*(5), 615–632.

Dulicai, D., Hays, R., & Nolan, P. (1989). Training the creative arts therapist: Identity with integration. *The Arts in Psychotherapy, 16*(1), 11–14.

Elkis-Abuhoff, D., Gaydos, M., Rose, S., & Goldblatt, R. (2010). The impact of education and exposure on art therapist identity and perception. *Art Therapy,: Journal of the American Art Therapy Association, 27*(3), 119–126.

Gerber, N. (2006). The essential components of doctoral-level education for art therapists. *The Arts in Psychotherapy, 33,* 98–112.

Kolb, D. (1984). *Experiential learning: Experience as the source of learning and development.* Upper Saddle River, NJ: Prentice Hall.

Marshall, J. (2007). Image as insight: Visual images in practice-based research. *Studies in Art Education, 49*(1), 23–41.

McAuliffe, G. (2000). How counselor education influences future helpers: What students say. In G. McAuliffe & K. Eriksen (Eds.), *Preparing counselors and therapists: Creating constructivist and developmental programs* (pp. 42–61). Virginia Beach, VA: Donning Publishers for the Association for Counselor Education and Supervision.

Orbiki, H. (2012). Students' artistic experience before and during graduate training. *The Arts in Psychotherapy, 39,* 428–435.

Rønnestad, M., & Skovholt, T. (2003). The journey of the counselor and therapist: Research findings and perspectives on professional development. *Journal of Career Development, 30*(1), 5–44.

Sullivan, G. (2006). Research acts in art practice. *Studies in Art Education, 48*(1), 19–35.

Walker, S. (2004). Understanding the art making process: Reflective practice. *Art Education, 57*(2), 6–12.

HOW CAN THE AMERICAN ART THERAPY ASSOCIATION GROW AND THRIVE?

Elizabeth Donahue, MA, LMHC, ATR

Where is the art therapy field now and where is it going? I have been thinking about this question for awhile, and I believe that it comes down to the issue of professional identity. The AATA has the opportunity to be a guiding force to help new graduates of art therapy programs to develop their professional identity. The AATA needs to attract and retain new art therapy professionals in order for the field to thrive in the future, and in order to do so, the AATA and the ATCB (Art Therapy Credentialing Board) must adapt and change to fit the needs of new art therapists.

Currently, it is expensive to earn and maintain the ATR credential.[1] Many new professionals must also maintain a state license or another professional credential in addition to the ATR in order to practice in (most) states in which it is not possible to obtain a license as an art therapist and they have to pay for these as well. High prices particularly in this difficult economy, are going to prohibit many art therapists from any involvement with AATA simply because it is not financially accessible for them and they can't afford to pay a membership fee on top of everything else. In addition, apparently the tangible benefits of AATA membership are few. Because much of the public doesn't know what ATR means, paying to maintain it becomes another expense with little obvious benefit.

Many art therapists graduate each year from master's-level education programs, nationally. However, many cannot afford to join AATA or choose not to for some other reason. I believe that without change and the ability to retain new members, the AATA will not grow and thrive in the future. I believe that AATA must evolve or it will whither away. I hope that the AATA can reduce the expense of membership-particularly for students and new graduates, or increase the benefits, or both. I hope that its leaders and members can make AATA what it should and could be—a major source of leadership, support, and interaction for the field.

One way to increase the benefit to members is to offer continuing education. The AATA could offer some form of low-cost, or dare I say

---

1. "ATR" is "Art Therapist Registered," a form of credentialing awarded by the ATCB.

free, continuing education. I think that it should provide regular ongoing free continuing education *on their website.* Another professional organization I know does this, and those that don't yet will probably be doing so in the future: Over a year, a member can get 12 continuing educations credits for free, and this benefits everyone-in participants' involvement with the organization, their level of new information and thus the increase in the quality in their work. Currently, the ATCB doesn't require CEUs[2] for art therapists to maintain their ATR, but it does for art therapists who become "Board Certified" (BC). The "ATR" is a requirement for the "BC." It has been a signification of quality and standards in the profession for many years and, if anything, has a more well-known meaning to the larger community. Relatively new, it is the intention of the ATCB to make the BC credential more important and standing for a higher level of quality. Unfortunately, because it is not much known to the public, this is a problem, and financially strapped art therapists may decide not to seek it at all. For those who are required to maintain another professional credential, the addition of more required CEUs is burdensome. If the AATA provides CEUs at low or no cost to members, it will reduce the cost of maintaining the BC credential while increasing the benefit of maintaining membership in AATA. This could be an important advantage to both new art therapists and the AATA.

Another example of the high cost of maintaining a connection with the AATA is the annual national conference. Attending a conference each year can be prohibitively expensive, especially when you include travel and lodging. This year it is in my town and down the street from where I live, so I don't have to travel or stay in a hotel, which helps with the expense, but my total ticket price for the conference is $600 (admission plus a few workshops, which are separately charged for). I think the conference should be free for students and new professionals and a good deal of "reaching out" by AATA should be provided for both. To be a member of the AATA would benefit art therapists to be able to stay close to community. It could also provide a sense of inclusion and ward against loneliness.

As to adding tangible benefit to membership in AATA, another option is to look at our online presence. Both the AATA and ATCB

---

2. "CEUs" are "Continuing Education Units," which are typically a requirement of maintaining many forms of mental health credentialing and state licensing to practice.

websites should be updated and improved. They look like they were created by people who didn't know a lot about technology and are not "user friendly." Newer art therapists are tech savvy and expect websites to deliver information efficiently and effectively. The current websites are cumbersome, and it is sometimes difficult to find necessary information. The websites could also function as a forum for new therapists to connect with each other and with seasoned professionals, with the use of an online message board. AATA could look to social media, such as Facebook and Twitter, for free and low-cost options for helping its members connect.

I find it is really hard to become an art therapist. First, there's an enormous amount of education necessary, and you may end up paying back student loans for a long time, but you're not done yet. After graduation, two years of supervision are required. These days this will cost the new graduate money, when, if they have found employment at all, it is hardly paying them a living wage. In my area, most new art therapists are not able to obtain onsite supervision with an ATR at their job, so they must pay out of pocket for private supervision. Employment has not caught up—it is tough to make a living wage in mental health today as a new graduate. Many are not able to afford private supervision and therefore never obtain their ATR. I was lucky to have a really great art therapist supervisor who helped me hold onto my art therapy identity as a new graduate, and I was lucky enough to get a discount, but ATRs are hard to find and pay for—even in my community which has had an art therapy program for a long time. I'm afraid the amount of money required makes the field classist, and it may appear to be a wealthy person's profession. What actually happens is that many art therapists fade away. They might go into being counselors and drop the art altogether. Some people from my graduate school cohort left the field entirely for this reason.

The AATA should be doing more to help educate the public about the practice of art therapy. While I understand the need for each art therapist to educate the public and that to be an art therapist includes an education function for the profession, I am personally extremely tired of educating about what an art therapist does. If I admit I am an art therapist, the next question is, "What's that?" Even in my first job, where I was hired specifically to be an art therapist, they didn't seem to understand art therapy, and I felt very alone. In order not to have to answer the question, sometimes I claim I am something else—then I feel guilty. Once I was on an airplane and a man said, "What do you do?" I really didn't want to explain, but I tried anyway. "Oh you work with kids? Is there play dough?" If AATA were able to help to spread the word to the public, individual art therapists might feel less alone. Again, social media may be of use to the association in addressing this issue.

The AATA has a responsibility to nurture its own, but I believe that universities and colleges where there are art graduate programs should also share in this task. Universities and colleges should offer a free group for graduates for at least two years, sponsored by the university or college program. It should meet regularly, but a minimum of once a month. It should be led by an experienced art therapist who has had some years of seasoning. It would include nurturing and clinical case supervision and help keep art therapists doing art therapy and staying in the community as they develop professionally. During graduate school, students receive plenty of nurturing and have like-minded colleagues who "speak the language." After graduation, the professionals are likely to be out there on their own. There should be more accessible ways of connecting with each other, and universities and AATA share the responsibility of facilitating this connection.

If new professionals can more easily make connections, the field of art therapy would begin to feel more like a community. Art therapists have a unique way of looking at the world, and it is important to have a venue to share this outlook with like-minded others.

The field of art therapy has evolved over the years and must continue to grow and change or risk the chance of withering away. The AATA has the opportunity to help the field thrive by attracting and retaining new art therapy professionals to its membership. To this end, reducing the cost and increasing the benefits of membership are necessary. My hope is that we can work together to accomplish these goals and that the future of art therapy is bright.

THE THERAPIST ARTIST:
AN INDIVIDUAL AND COLLECTIVE WORLDVIEW

Nancy Gerber, PhD, ATR-BC, LPC

The identity of the art therapist is an intriguing topic that I think requires reflection, particularly in our contemporary sociopolitical and economic climate. Reflection allows us to thoughtfully reconsider long-held personal and collective beliefs, cultural attitudes and practices, and shifting societal contexts and worldviews. I have been thinking about this topic for several months, ever since I was asked to write this essay, and I have developed a few ideas that I will discuss here. I approach this task by first exploring some ideas about the formation of our individual professional identities and subsequently positing some hypotheses about the philosophical assumptions that I think contribute to the formation of our collective identities within current cultural contexts.

Personal Identity as an Art Therapist

Each of us has a personal story about how and why we became art therapists and how those life decisions have contributed to our personal and professional identities. So I thought I would begin by revisiting my own story. The process of reminiscing was a creative one, which led me from reflection on my personal art therapy story to musings about my broader personal philosophy about art therapy. These two processes, which I call *the formative years* and *the therapist as artist,* have resulted in a re-visiting and re-construction of my ideas about what I value about art therapy and therefore what is central to my art therapy identity.

My Formative Years

Stories about our professional choices and identities are multi-determined, including the dynamic interaction among biopsychosocial, conscious, and unconscious influences. The formation of my own art therapy identity, which I consciously recall, began 39 years ago just prior to my entry into a graduate school art therapy program. Of course, the powerful, personal unconscious influences that led me to choose that path began much earlier in my life. Those unconscious influences were probably what attracted me to a field for which I felt a visceral affinity but about which I had minimal actual knowledge. It was an intuitive attraction similar to love at first sight. I was introduced to art therapy in the early 1970s, when I was volunteering at a suicide help line. While there I had been told by some friends, who were psychiatric residents in training at Hahnemann Medical College and Hospital[1] that they thought I had a gift for talking to people about profound psychological problems. As I talked more to these friends, they learned of my background in art education and mentioned that a new graduate program in a new field called art therapy had just been initiated several years earlier at Hahnemann. Coincidentally, at the same time of this conversation, I had become disillusioned with my work as an art teacher; I saw so many troubled kids who succeeded brilliantly in communicating through their art but were failing miserably in their academic studies. These kids related to the world through a form of cognition that was not readily understood, acknowledged, or accepted in the dominant culture of education or society—the plight of artists since the beginning of time! I was frustrated by the lack of value assigned to the arts within the educational system, particularly for these kids. Subsequently, I resigned my position after writing a rather self-righteous diatribe to the school board about their obvious oversight relative to the contributions of the arts to the psychological, academic, and social well-being of us humans and these kids.

Accentuated by my teaching experience was an already gnawing vague and uneducated notion—that the arts were such an important vehicle for telling the untellable stories that exist beyond the tangible and the immediately visible-giving life and expression to the silent soul. As I learned more about art therapy, I realized that to me this was the essence of art therapy—it resonated with me and became the heart of my identity as an art therapist. I realized that art therapy used a way of knowing that valued images, and other pre-verbal phenomena, as the language of the human mind and as an x-ray of the human soul. Over the years, I have come to regard this most intimate, multidimensional and essential communication of emotional human experience

---

1. Hahnemann has had a name change to "Drexel."

through the language of imagery as the phenomenon of aesthetic inter-subjectivity. Aesthetic intersubjective communication is what allows for the emergence and telling of a personal illustrated story in which the past and present co-exist while we also re-imagine and re-create ourselves in the presence of an attentive witness participant.

The vignette I have presented is a brief snippet from a long career as an art therapist, but recalling it led me to more thoughtful reflection on my identity as a person and an art therapist. Therefore, in considering our personal art therapy identities, perhaps it behooves us all to dedicate some thoughtful reflection and courageous exploration of our own personal psychological intersubjective aesthetic histories and stories. Our personal intersubjective aesthetic stories are a powerful influence on how and why we practice art therapy and our capacity to attune to others' histories and stories.

The Therapist Artist

A central idea emerging from the thoughtful reflection about my own art therapy identity is that I consider myself to be a *therapist artist*—or, in other words, *my artistry exists in the art of art therapy.* In becoming an art therapist, my passion and priority was developing myself as an artist whose medium was art therapy—a creative art form in and of its own right. The art of art therapy exists in the co-creation of an aesthetic life narrative that emerges within the intersubjective context of the therapeutic relationship. This aesthetic co-created narrative manifests as a psychological portrait of a person's life painted in a language of hieroglyphics. The art therapist participates in the co-creation and sensitive decoding of this life portrait and gives it new meaning. In this process, the art therapist uses all of her or his theoretical knowledge, self/other presence, and knowledge as an artist. Symington (1996) elaborated on this concept, positing that the joint creation of this pictorial narrative, consisting of both the patient and the therapist images, is the re-telling of the patient's story *through imagination.* The use of imagination and re-creation of the patient's story within a therapeutic relationship allows a new clarity, pattern, and form to emerge from what was previously chaos. "My central point is that it is through the imagination that the meaningful world as we know it is constructed" (Symington, 1996, p. 38).

Central to this concept of art therapy as an art form and therapist as artist are two major phenomena—intersubjective aesthetic knowledge and the "dialectical edge" (Israelstam, 2007, p. 594). Artists and psychotherapists by nature have open access to their own and others' unconscious aesthetic knowledge by which they touch, express, transform, and communicate the most essential of human experience in their art form. This requires imagination, curiosity, and an aesthetic sense (Harris-Williams, 2010; Symington, 1996). I call this intersubjective aesthetic knowledge. *Aesthetics* is defined in this context based on the Greek translation meaning "perception" (Cooper, 2006, p. 1) or "sense-based awareness" (Harris Williams, 2010, p. xiii), which is used to convey the preverbal sensory, kinesthetic, imaginal, and emotional intersubjective experience as expressed symbolically and artistically within in a relationship. Robbins (1988) called this phenomenon "psychoaesthetics"(Gerber, in press).

The intersubjective aspect of aesthetic knowledge implies that aesthetic knowledge develops and is influenced by a self/other context as early as first infant/mother communications (Dissanayake, 2009; Robbins, 2000; Winnicott, cited in Ogden, 1990). Consequently, this imaginative way of being and knowing not only is the necessary ingredient for creativity in artistic expression but is also essential for attuning to understanding and empathizing with the early pre-verbal emotional experience of another human being. The therapist engages in similar imaginative processes as the artist, but instead of the dialogue between artist and art medium, the therapist shifts the dialogue to that among and between people. The therapeutic relational or potential space (Ogden, 1990) becomes the empty canvas or the lump of clay. The art therapist uses their aesthetic sense to enter and attune to the emotional, pre-verbal consciousness of the patient and engages her or him in co-constructing an illustrative narrative on this empty shared canvas or re-forming the lump of clay.

The psychological artifacts unearthed during the intersubjective aesthetic process are fragments representing *a seemingly nonsensical world of the unconscious.* What emerges are flickers, snapshots, and sensations representing precious artifacts of a human psychological experience. To understand the irrationality of the human mind and the way in which a human story develops over time from pre-verbal intersubjective ways of knowing requires mindful creativity. It is here that the therapist artist is able to respect these psychological artifacts, often in the form of images, viewing them as chaotic puzzle pieces that when artfully assembled, will emerge as a co-created painted or sculpted story ready for telling and meaning making. If the art therapist is receptive to the idiosyncratic language communicated through image and sensation induced in the therapist, then the art therapist is poised at a point of unparalleled privilege-to witness and collaborate to make meaning of these hieroglyphic messages for the patient. As Meltzer (cited in Harris-Williams, 2010) said, "The 'poet' takes over from the neurophysiologist . . . and Freud as clinician becomes 'an artist at work,' able to follow the method and the patient and to tolerate not understanding what was happening" (p. xx). The therapist is artist.

Complementary and necessary to the intersubjective aesthetic sensibility, which allows the therapist artist to attune to and navigate between these multiple states of consciousness, is the capacity to perch on and live in the precarious emotional tightrope between metaphysical and paradoxical psychological worlds (Israelstam, 2007; Robbins, 1988, 2000). Balancing on what Israelstam (2007) calls the "creative dialectical edge" (p. 594) requires the suspension of time, space, and logic as well as embracing the surreal paradoxical co-existence of contradictory ideas and concepts. This "dialectical edge" generates authentic intersubjective aesthetic data, which then become the essence of the psychological portrait and ultimately the therapy. This ability to participate in the creative dialectical process–constant movement between different levels of consciousness and unconsciousness between madness and sanity, me and not me (Winnicott, cited in Israelstam, 2007) while remaining present and poised on the "creative dialectical edge" (Israelstam, 2007, p. 594), is at the center of the artist's, therapist's, and therapist artist's psychological makeup and identity.

To summarize, the therapist artist possesses an intersubjective aesthetic sensibility that allows her or him to touch essential remote and precious forms of human knowledge and experience in themselves and others. This sensibility, in combination with the capacity to enter the human unconscious, to remain perched on and tolerant of the dangerous ambiguity of the "dialectical edge" and to co-create a meaningful illustrative human story from the psychological artifacts, is essential to the art therapist's spirit and identity.

Philosophy and Worldview

The process of reflecting on my own story led to reflections on perspectives that could inform the collective identity or worldview. The therapist artist, within which the phenomena of intersubjective aesthetic sensibility and the creative "dialectical edge" (Israelstam, 2007, p. 594) exist, embodies the qualities and aptitudes of what occurs in the therapy session. But there are other external pragmatic variables that contribute to the formation of our individual and collective art therapist identities. These pragmatic variables of cultural norms and values, systems and organizational dynamics, legal and ethical guidelines, interact with those of the therapist artist and contribute to the construction of my overall philosophy or worldview (Gerber, in press.) This philosophy includes conscious and unconscious individual and collective beliefs, assumptions, theories, and values that influence our perspectives, behaviors, and professional practice. Because these core assumptions and values are so influential in our professional lives, I believe in actively exploring, knowing, and articulating not only our individual philosophy but also a collective professional philosophy and worldview for our field. The rationale for identifying our essential philosophy is that it helps us remain anchored in the moral, ethical, and theoretical value system on which our professional practice is based. The discovery and attunement to this anchored value system also allows us to critically evaluate, integrate, or reject new knowledge, fads, trends, cultural and societal shifts, or regulatory currents that either contribute or detract from our central mission as art therapists.

As an art therapist, my identity exists around the essential philosophical assumption that art therapy *acknowledges and embraces multiple inter- and intra-psychic or intersubjective realities in the pursuit of psychological truth and creative freedom.* The nature of knowledge that exists in these multiple realities, and which is used to pursue our psychological truths, includes sensory, emotional, kinesthetic, and imaginal or aesthetic intersubjective ways of knowing. Finally, as an art therapist, I place value on these multiple realities and forms of knowledge, in that these ways of being and knowing lead to a more fulfilling self and self/other aware and creative life. Living a creative and free life is best described by Lear (1998), who says of philosophy and psychoanalysis and, I would add, art therapy, "that they are forms of life committed to living openly—with truth, beauty, envy and hate, wonder, awe and dread" (p. 5).

Based on the identification of these aesthetic and dialectical forms of knowledge and the multiple inter- and intra-psychic and intersubjective realities in which they exist, we can begin to formulate a more collective philosophy and worldview.

Collective Identity–Philosophy and Worldview

As I have made clear, my contention is that the dialogue about professional identity, as rooted in our collective philosophical assumptions or worldview, is one that requires attention, particularly today in a world dominated by hegemonies and unstable fluid regulatory issues that affect perceptions of legitimacy, efficacy, and the economy. We live in a culture in which efficacy, legitimacy, and value are often determined by an assumed but unspoken reality that is visible, singular, and tangible. Within this version of reality is the assumption that logical, causal, and measureable knowledge is equated with a singular truth and thus assigned the highest value resulting in economic decisions that affect research and employment (Gerber, 2004).

Given the power and dominance of this worldview, it behooves us to examine how it fits with and influences the worldview of our own profession. As we make crucial decisions about the future of our profession related to accreditation, licensure, education, and research dictated by a dominant worldview, we need to carefully assess how these decisions reflect and affect the essential philosophy of our profession and how much they reflect and affect a betrayal of those principles in favor of those of the dominant worldview. As a profession with a valuable perspective on the realities and knowledge of human motivation, behavior, creativity, and life quality, it would be a mistake, and I believe unethical, to abandon these philosophical and practical perspectives and make crucial decisions based on fear, intimidation, and desperation.

By automatically submitting to a dominant worldview in attempts to satisfy external legislative and regulatory bodies without systematically examining how such decisions impact our philosophy, identity, and, most importantly, our contribution to our fellow humans can be a lethal mistake for art therapy. But if we carefully examine the shared phil-

osophical assumptions and worldview that form our collective identity, we can engage in informed conversations with each other, with other professions, legislators, and stakeholders while remaining clear in
our identity and mission–to rehabilitate, educate, cooperate, and leg-
islate. Lear (1998) cautions about fields like ours in succumbing to the
temptation of becoming too dogmatic or standardized as prescribed
by regulatory organizations: "Can philosophy become 'concrete' without itself disappearing? And if all that is left is, say, empirical psychology, has psychology itself survived?" (p. 8). He continues to say that,
"we want to pass on fundamental truths and in our attempts to do so
truth becomes rigid and dies" (Lear, 1998, p. 6).

In pursuit of the goal of carefully and systematically exploring our
philosophy and identity, we might heed Socrates' words–"the unex-
amined life is not worth living" (cited in Lear, 1998, p. 4). I would challenge us to consider Socrates' words and examine the life and identity
of our profession so as not to unknowingly destroy it. In the previous
section, I have referenced a worldview or paradigm. As we explore
the philosophy and identity of our profession I, suggest using a paradigmatic or worldview construct, borrowed from the realm of social
and behavioral science research, as a guide to examining, not dogma-
tizing, the embedded philosophical assumptions of our profession's
life and identity.

Art Therapy Worldview or Paradigm

The terms *worldview* and *paradigm* are often used interchangeably to
mean a perspective, system of beliefs or philosophical assumptions,
and sensibilities that influence research questions, design, and methodology (Creswell & Plano-Clark, 2001; Mertens, 2005). For example,
we might say the dominant culture within our Western society is best
represented by a more positivist or post-positivist worldview while that
of our profession, the minority culture, might be best represented by a
constructivist or dialectical constructivist worldview (Gerber, 2004, in
press; Greene, 2007). The *positivist or post-positivist worldview regards the
nature of reality or truth as consisting of the natural physical and social constructs existing in the universe* (Paul, Graffam, & Fowler, 2005, p. 46), and
argues, we might say, that this is a reality "knowable within probabil-
ity" (Mertens, 2005, p. 9). In contrast, the *constructivist paradigm em-*

braces *"multiple socially constructed realities"* (Mertens, 2005, p.9) *in which knowledge is the "dynamic product of the interactive work of the mind"* (Paul, Graffam, & Fowler, 2005, p. 46). It is emergent within intersubjective, social, and cultural contexts. *Adding the dialectical aspect to this constructivist worldview allows for the dynamic and creative interplay between multiple paradigms and methods of inquiry* depending on the nature of the knowledge being investigated. The dialectic provides a creative and dynamic model for simultaneously entertaining "multiple mental models [which] offer many different ways of seeing and knowing" (Greene, 2007, p. 79). Furthermore, the "tensions created by juxtaposing different paradigms, to achieve dialectical discovery of enhanced, reframed or new understandings" results in new knowledge (Greene, 2007, p. 69). *Dialecticism allows for moving among different levels of consciousness, entertaining ambiguity, and a consideration that all forms of paradoxical knowledge are sources of new knowledge.* Not only does this dialectical constructivist paradigm provide a philosophy compatible with the origins and theories in the arts therapies, it also allows for an inclusiveness of diverse perspectives both within and outside of our profession (Gerber, in press).

From this perspective and using this lens, we can begin to see that the worldview by which we as art therapists operate is slightly different from that of the dominant culture. Most of us know this intuitively or viscerally, but we need to be able to know it in a way that we can articulate, discuss, and negotiate. So, by consciously re-visiting the central philosophical assumptions that are embedded in our history and collective unconscious, we can begin to identify and more clearly articulate our worldview. The paradigm used by multiple researchers to systematically examine philosophical assumptions includes four major philosophical areas: (a) ontology, (b) epistemology, (c) axiology, and (d,) methodology. *Ontology* refers to the assumptions about how we define the nature of reality or truth. *Epistemology* refers to the nature of knowledge or how we know what we know. *Axiology* refers to our ethics or values relative to this knowledge. *Methodology* refers to how we investigate these assumptions (Mertens, 2005; Paul et al., 2005). Based on this paradigm, I would like to initiate a conversation in which we explore these philosophical assumptions relevant to art therapy.

In art therapy, *ontologically,* we embrace multiple and interactive realities that are inter-, intra-psychically and intersubjectively constructed. Referred to as "ontological pluralism" (Johnson & Gray, 2010, p. 72), this view lends itself well to the *epistemology* of art therapy, in which knowledge includes multiple dynamic, dialectic, aesthetic, and intersubjective ways of knowing (Gerber, in press). In art therapy, our knowledge is filled with ambiguity and paradox, wherein the real exists alongside the surreal, the self co-mingles with the other, the logical and linear interact with the irrational and chaotic, and time and space are coexistent timelessness and infinity. The *axiological* aspect of our worldview articulates what we value and what is ethical within our philosophical assumptions. For instance, Paul et al. (2005), cite the values from an Interpretivist perspective–to "recover the moral importance and imagination of the social sciences in order to create change in the world" (p. 47). In art therapy, we might adopt a similar *axiology,* but it should be one in which we emphasize our strong belief in the value of how aesthetic knowledge in pursuit of self-awareness within an intersubjective context contributes to health, freedom, and creativity on both individual and collective cultural levels.

Summarily, as we explore our individual and collective art therapy worldviews, we can begin as a profession to clearly decide what our philosophical position is and, I believe, more thoughtfully and responsibly make decisions about how we are to exist in and respond to an increasingly regulatory culture, as well as communicate and collaborate with our professional colleagues who may have differing worldviews. By formulating and looking at our professional identity through what could be called a *creative dialectical constructivist paradigmatic* lens, or any other appropriate philosophical perspective, I think we can remain centered in the underlying values and principles that make art therapy what it is, and we can therefore confidently negotiate with the regulatory external world without compromising the essential integrity of the field. Art therapy's engaging in this process of exploring, creating, and adopting a structural worldview as a profession, I would propose, only strengthens our collective and individual identities and also provides us with a strong and clear vision of who we are within our culture and society.

References

Cooper, D. (Ed.) (1997). *Aesthetics: The classic readings.* Malden, MA: Blackwell Publishing.

Creswell, J., & Plano-Clark, V. (2011). *Designing and conducting mixed methods research* (2nd ed.). Thousand Oaks, CA: Sage.

Dissanayake, E. (2009). The artification hypothesis and its relevance to cognitive science, evolutionary aesthetics and neuroaesthetics. *Cognitive Semiotics, 5,* 148–173. Available at http://www.ellendissanayake.com/publications/

Gerber, N. (2004). The essential components of doctoral level education for art therapists. Unpublished doctoral dissertation. Retrieved from ProQuest (ID3050 50496).

Gerber, N. (in press). Art therapy education: A creative dialectic intersubjective approach. In M. Rosal & D. Gussack (Eds.), *Handbook of art therapy.* Oxford, UK: Wiley Blackwell.

Greene, J. (2007). *Mixed methods in social inquiry.* San Francisco, CA: Jossey-Bass.

Hagman, G. (1994). Aesthetic experience: Beauty, creativity and the search for the ideal. Amsterdam, the Netherlands: Rodopi. B.V.

Harris Williams, M. (2010). *The aesthetic development: The poetic spirit of psychoanalysis.* London: Karnac Books.

Israelstam, K. (2007). Creativity and dialectical phenomena: From dialectical edge to dialectical space. *International Journal of Psychoanalysis, 88,* 591–607.

Johnson, R., & Gray, R. (2010). A history of philosophical and theoretical issues for mixed methods research. In A. Tashakkori & C. Teddlie (Eds.), *Mixed methods in social & behavioral research* (pp. 69–94). Thousand Oaks, CA: Sage.

Lear, J. (1998). *Open minded: Working ou the logic of the soul.* Cambridge, MA: Harvard University Press.

Meadows, P. (2000). Creating psychic change in analysis. *Modern Psychoanalysis, 25*(1), 3–21.

Mertens, D. (2005). *Research and evaluation in education and psychology: Integrating diversity with quantitative, qualitative, and mixed methods* (2nd ed.). Thousand Oaks, CA: Sage.

Ogden, T. (1990). *The matrix of the mind: Object relations and the psychoanalytic dialogue.* Northvale, NJ: Jason Aronson.

Paul, J., Graffam, B., & Fowler, K. (2005). Perspectivism and critique of research: An overview. In J. Paul (Ed.), *Introduction to the philosophies of research and criticism in education and the social sciences* (pp. 43–65). Upper Saddle River, NJ: Pearson Prentice Hall.

Robbins. A. (1988). A psychoaesthetic perspective on creative arts therapy and training. *The Arts in Psychotherapy, 15,* 95–100.

Robbins, A. (2000). *The artist as therapist.* Philadelphia, PA: Jessica Kingsley Publishers.

Symington, N. (1996). *The making of a psychotherapist.* Madison, CT: International Universities Press.

IDENTITY AND THE SERENDIPITOUS ART THERAPIST

David E. Gussak, PhD, ATR-BC

When Dr. Junge asked for a contribution to her text on the identity of the art therapist, I assumed it would be a fairly straightforward task, but it wasn't. Over the years, I have struggled with the question of professional identity, for the art therapist and for the field. This search culminated in my dissertation study (Gussak, 2001), and several articles, including a response to the question of whether art therapy is an idea or a profession (Gussak, 2000) and the gender identity of being a male art therapist (Gussak, 2008). However, like all self-evaluations, viewpoints evolve, solidify, fragment and change, making this much more difficult than originally anticipated. To facilitate this essay process, a current graduate student, Jaimie Burkowitz, conducted an interview with me using questions Dr. Junge provided as a starting point.

Once the interview began, Ms. Burkowitz pursued the emerging ideas through further inquiry. This resulted in what I believe to be a dynamic interchange. To best communicate these ideas, this essay is presented as a dialogue. Consequently, the statements may be rife with colloquialisms and informalities; those have been left in the text to maintain the sense of this dialogue about identity-one that I think is essential, not just with our new students and emerging art therapists but also with ourselves.

JB: So what first interested you in art therapy as a career choice?

DG: I think that is an important question to begin this exploration because how people choose this field always begins with identity. I did not know that there was a field of art therapy before I thought about becoming an art therapist. The only high school course I did well in was art. My art teacher Jay Palefsky suggested that because I liked people, I could use art to help others—perhaps become an art therapist. We both thought we made up the term, but I soon discovered there was such a thing when I attended an art therapy workshop my first year in college. I became entranced.

I took an art therapy undergraduate course from Dr. Nancy Knapp; at the time, I was working in a psychiatric facility. If I was to pursue art therapy as a career, I had to find a program that allowed me to work, as I needed to put myself through school. Nancy told me about Vermont College's program—it enabled me to take classes in the summer and work during the school year, *and* its focus corresponded with my understandings of mental health.

Growing up, the idea of even going to graduate school was antithetic to anything I ever imagined before, so it was quite a surprise, but it worked out beautifully. Following graduation, I secured a job in a prison.

In 1997, after teaching workshops, lecturing for various educational programs, and actively serving the art therapy community, I decided I wanted to go into higher education. I began pursuing positions that were available, and I secured my first teaching post at Emporia State University where Nancy Knapp was then the director; it was something I serendipitously fell into. How I ended up becoming an art therapist, working with the prison population, serving the field, were all through happenstance. Everything happened at crossroads, allowing me to make decisions to pursue what I loved doing.

JB: After working with the prison population, I'm curious whether you agree that art therapy is part of the mental health pantheon rather than rehabilitation or educational, occupational therapy, or recreational activity. Dr. Junge noted that some thought it too close to the "medical model" and too "clinified." Do you think defining art therapy, as a mental health discipline, should still be the major thrust for art therapy?

DG: I believe there is a philosophical and pragmatic issue about professional identity. While I think that an art therapist can work in many arenas, I have pursued my own place in this field in a manner that allowed me to be clinical in the mental health arena. When I worked in prisons, my job title was "rehabilitation therapist/art therapist," and I worked closely with music, recreation, and occupational therapists [not a mental health job description]. I knew that I had to pragmatically accept this title to work, but I held onto my clinical identity, through writing, presenting, and ultimately teaching.

I think art therapy's identity in the mental health arena gives it a niche, acknowledging that we have clinical skills and use art as the tools that create a psychological means of reaching our clients when others may not available. So I do think that art provides us an end road to psychological and mental health development.

*JB: I'm curious also about identity problems. "What identity problems are cre-
ated by the current umbrella with many definitions model within the art therapy community?" Do you think [the field] could benefit from a stable unified
identity and why?*

DG: No. I think our identity is often determined from within as much
as by others. Art therapists may at times disagree with one another
about what may be considered the "correct" or "incorrect" way of doing
things. My dissertation explored this notion (Gussak, 2001). Its impetus
was if you put five art therapists in a room together and you ask them
what they did and why it worked, would it be clear that each one of
them did something different to reach the same end result? This hypothesis led to questioning what happens and how art therapy theory
translates into practice. What emerged was that theory seemed to give
way to practice within six months to a year of an art therapist leaving
an educational program. The system of art therapy helps shape the work,
re-creating the vocabulary used and the identity created. It's a hard
road, and some may fight it, but many develop a necessary flexible identity in order to practice and provide care for clients.
Initially, theory may inform practice, but eventually theory and practice
co-evolve, so practice re-informs theory and theory helps re-develop
practice-it is a never-ending cycle. Art therapists are usually creative
enough to know when to adapt. Even in the middle of treatment, it becomes easier to shift directions, and that becomes part of the identity.
Eventually how we care for our clients becomes intuitive, and we may
not realize until afterward what theory may best be used to explain
what was done.

*JB: Does it matter for art therapists to engage in art? What does making art
have to do with the personal/professional identity of the art therapist?*

DG: As art therapists, I think it is our responsibility to continue to
engage in the arts, and it is part of our identity to know how materials
may affect clients. If we are to understand the power of art with our
clients, then we need to engage in it ourselves, and, quite frankly, I
think it hypocritical of us not to do our own art when we require it of
our clients. Otherwise art is an insular part of the treatment and becomes secondary. If we are just using art as an impetus to get people to
talk, then you might as well have them twiddle their thumbs or knit. If
you do not know the value of doing art and if you do not experience
the power of the art or trust the art-making process, then you might as

well not even use it. In some environments, talking during the sessions may not even be encouraged. For example, when I was an art therapist in a prison, I soon learned that it was best for the inmates *not* to talk, as giving voice to weakness and vulnerability may be taken advantage of by other inmates. In an environment where survival of the fittest was the rule, the non-verbal characteristics of the art therapy sessions allowed a therapeutic process to occur without having to put it into words. While it is important to know how to use words in a therapeutic context, the question still remains: If a client does not speak during a session, does art therapy still work? An effective art therapist would have to answer "yes"; that the art itself, with the art therapist serving as an auxiliary ego, holding environment, or cognitive support, however you want to describe it, may facilitate a treatment trajectory. That is what makes us different from other therapists and, dare I say it, more complicated.

JB: Who or what do you think should be responsible for defining art therapy professional identity? Does the art therapy profession mostly define itself or does it mostly allow others to define it?

DG: Assuming that we have a profession.

JB: Are you saying that because you view us as still being in the process of "forming of idea" stage within our profession?

DG: We make the mistake of thinking that since we have a professional organization we have a defined profession. Art therapists have an idea of what art therapy is and what it entails; this idea is surrounded by professionals who create an invisible college: "Art therapy as an idea was the crux that helped form a [professional] organization despite divergent viewpoints"(Gussak, 2000, p. 5). It's not a vague notion, yet the specific meaning of art therapy varies. We are not ready to say that we are a profession as much as we believe in what art therapy has to offer; we maintain clear guidelines in how to provide services in a professional, ethical manner; this does not necessarily make us a profession.

That is not to say anyone can do art therapy. It requires specific training and knowledge. Art therapists are trained to facilitate the art process for therapeutic gain. We need to shout from the hilltops that to be an art therapist requires a specialized education; that is, a combination of clinical, medical, rehabilitation, and—most importantly—art.

It is our responsibility to maintain a clear identity when we face out-ward; it is okay for us to wrestle with our identity internally, to deal with the nuanced (or not so subtle) differences between the members of this invisible college. Yet when facing outward, external forces may in turn define us. We need to provide a clear, distinct image, and display and celebrate our similarities and consistencies.

JB: In what way does current art therapy education contribute to or make dif-ficult art therapy identity formation and what should it do?

DG: In order to maintain consistency and validity, there needs to be identifiable curricula across all art therapy educational programs. As long as they adopt a sound scaffold, it is up to the programs to then focus and delineate any type of infrastructure within their program for their own specific identity and then let the buyer (i.e., students), deter-mine what works best for them. The variety in the programs often re-flects the various theoretical identities we maintain in our field, and art therapy programs may be very different from each other.
The other side of this question is that some programs have dual degrees. This creates a struggle between philosophical idealism and pragmatic necessity and maintaining art therapist identity as a specific type of clin-ician. However, I think for art therapy to survive its dilution or absorp-tion by other fields, while still creating relationships with them, these dual-degree options should be considered nothing more than a means to provide additional tools.

JB: As our teacher, it seems you help us grasp all of these theories so that we can start to form a sensible scaffolding as to what art therapy is and then hopefully form our own theories of what art therapy is, realizing along the way that every person is different and therefore not every method will apply to everyone. We must be knowledgeable to be flexible.

DG: I think so. Of course, there may be resistance. It is similar to break-ing down the ego to re-build a healthier one: We may have to break down students' myths to re-create their view as professionals. By the time the students get to their second year in our graduate program, they understand their first responsibility is meeting the needs of their client. They also learn they will be in environments and systems where people do not always like or understand what they do. Some of these environ-ments may not even know what art therapy is or they may have a wrong perspective about it.

Art therapy education should not only prepare students to meet their clients' needs but also to work within systems. It must prepare them for the clinical experience so that they are able to explain and sometimes defend themselves through identity and demonstration. Becoming aware of legislation and how it pertains to art therapists is also an essential task of student art therapists. This can benefit not only the client but the field as a whole. In addition, I believe it is the ethical responsibility of educators to help graduates find employment after they graduate.

JB: One of Dr. Junge's earlier questions is, "What would it take for art therapy to move past the dialectic/duality models of psychology/art (Naumburg/Kramer) of the past, which she believes may imply the adversarial right and wrong, into a less confusing and cooperative model?" I'm wondering if you think that this is still going on.

DG: I appreciate that question as I find this right/wrong business an archaic concept. The notion that we have a bipolar identity of art as therapy/art psychotherapy is just a tiny fragment of the system that we belong to. There are many different interconnected nodules on the outside of our circle. Any one of us could take any of these identities and concepts and create a new definition or identity in our field. It is not adversarial, although there are some members of the field who may not always appreciate others' approaches or identities. One person may be more artistic, creative, ethereal, or esoteric; one might be more cognitive, clinical, empirical, or quantitative; and one may be more involved in the medical or rehabilitation field. It is not my place to say that any one is more accurate than another. I do know where I stand among these continua. It is incorrect to think our relationships in this field are bipolar rather than a series of various intersecting criteria that allow us to be what we need to be at any given moment.

JB: Do you believe that this is the general consensus of all art therapists?

DG: There is never going to be a general consensus.

JB: Could a goal of AATA be to make art therapy more applicable to the general population and to raise awareness in the different ways art therapy can be used? Like promoting art therapists' books, publishing in non-art therapy journals, marketing and advertising, anything to make aware the research being done, and that we are an evolving and powerful field applicable to several areas. I just keep thinking everything is so contained within the art therapy field. The only

people who really read the journal and receive the articles are other art thera-
pists; what about everyone else? Do we need a public relations initiative?

DG: To be clear, although it is the oldest art therapy professional organization in the United States at this time, AATA is not the only one. In
my opinion, AATA's role is to protect our image, work closely with like-
missioned cohorts (other creative art therapy groups, counseling organizations, etc.), and sew together interrelationships in order for us to develop, maintain, expand, and protect our identity. As much as they are
responsible for reaching out to other organizations, to a certain extent,
AATA's role is to also keep us insular so that we can project a clear identity and stay strong within.

 If we want to get the word out, we have to be able to speak in a manner that people outside of our field can understand. We run the risk of
speaking a language that other people cannot understand, forcing us to
become too inbred. The result could be that we are only preaching to
the choir. Hence, we should simultaneously disseminate our information and absorb information from others–this may create more hetero-
geneous interconnectivity and a much more dynamic and sustaining field.
Too long, we have been talking to ourselves at our own conferences and
publishing in our own journals; we have been visible to ourselves, but
perhaps not to others. Nonetheless, some of us have successfully ven-
tured outward, publishing articles in other professional journals, writing
books with more diverse publishing foci, and presenting at various
venues that are not art therapy. We write about what we do and we learn
to write in a language that others understand. We provide viable information that can, in turn, further our identity through scholarly discourse.
What we write is just as important as how we write. Where we present
and publish enables us to celebrate our identity and make art therapy
familiar to others. But we have to be prepared to accept others' work in
outside fields. It is not enough to speak out; we need to learn to listen
in (Gussak & Orr, 2005).

JB: It sounds like you suggest that collaborations could be beneficial to art ther-
apy as a field and for its identity, so we should be willing to work with a team
of people in related fields?

DG: I agree. I remember there was one AATA journal issue that came
out a couple years ago in which there were no articles written by an art
therapist. While I think this is a problem, generally, I do not see anything wrong with us including articles that are written by people outside

the field. These collaborative efforts can demonstrate how all can meet the needs of our clients.

JB: Do you think the art therapists' attainment of licensure [as art therapists] could impact our legitimacy and credibility within other mental health care arenas?

DG: Although I see licensure as valuable, as has been clear with my past legislative efforts for various states and AATA, I think we are too stuck on the term *licensure.* I believe we should focus on "legislative identity" without the necessity of having to pursue a license every time. I believe credentials are important, but people tend to think a license is going to be the panacea to help them get a job or third-party [health insurance] reimbursement. Art therapists need to be reminded that a credential actually is intended to protect the public, so that people know when they are bringing on an art therapist who has a particular credentialed designation, they have been put through certain trials to demonstrate knowledge and currency, so the client knows what they are getting. Credentialing provides accountability. I urge strengthening the identity and visibility of our own credentials.

We can continue to support state identity and state legislative actions while also understanding that there is a national professional organization in place to help act as the scaffolding. Perhaps such scaffolding may be all that is in place for states that cannot get legislative identity. But art therapists need to do what they can to strengthen their place in the arena, and sometimes that means compromise.

JB: As a professional membership organization, do you consider the AATA members mostly competitive or mostly cooperative?

DG: Both. I think that AATA is competitive and cooperative in as much as our members have competitive or cooperative personalities. Some of us are territorial and some of us are not. I do not think AATA pushes one way or another. Personally I like to think I am cooperative, but other people may disagree. The organization is the macro-system of the art therapy profession or identity—an extension of who we are. We have created the organization that identifies us as best as it can. AATA does not create us; we create AATA. We have met the enemy, and they are us.

References

Gussak, D. (2000). The invisible college of art therapy professionals. *Art Therapy: Journal of the American Art Therapy Association, 17*(1), 4–6.

Gussak, D. (2001). *The work of the art therapist: An Interactionist perspective.* Unpublished doctoral dissertation, Emporia State University, Emporia, KS.

Gussak, D., & Orr, P. (2005). Ethical responsibilities: Preparing students for the real art therapy world. *Art Therapy: Journal of the American Art Therapy Association, 22*(2), 101–104.

ART THERAPIST IDENTITY

Janice Hoshino, PhD, ATR-BC, LMFT

I believe it is interesting to consider identity formation for the entire art therapy community from how they first learned about art therapy and how their early experiences informed their decision to become an art therapist. For me (and I suspect, for others), the elements that are important derive from the beginnings of my life. Some of the specific elements instilled in me through the environment in which I grew up particularly focused on the human condition and humanity.

I grew up on state hospital grounds in Pennsylvania; my father was a staff member. The house I lived in was the original gatekeeper's house facing the main gates of the institution and first intended as a place to investigate or watch out for the asylum patients. The house was built in 1860 for observing potential escaped patients. As I was growing up in the 1960s and 1970s, of course, the gates were open, but my early identity and my personal identity really became linked with the state hospital community.

Growing up on the grounds, the other kids and I would use the hundreds of acres, including a farm and green house, as a playground, and we often saw patients out working with the farm animals or gardening, so patients and kids were interactive. There was no fear of one another; it was a community that seemed normal to me.

As I grew older, I realized that this lack of fear was not the case with the larger world outside the state hospital. The state hospital was a sheltered community separate from the community outside its gates. It occurred to me as I grew up that the outside world really did not enter the state hospital community unless they were employed or committed there.

One of my early experiences, at around seven or eight years of age, was when a patient escaped. No one could find the patient. What was so interesting to me was that the people in the outside community–parents of my classmates and "respectable citizens"–began what we would call "a manhunt." With bats and guns, they scoured the neighborhood trying to find the escapee. The state hospital police finally found the patient: He had climbed up a tree and was viewing the neighborhood hunting him down; he was terrified, so he stayed in the tree until someone spotted him.

I had come in contact with a powerful and poignant experience, which taught me how much the mentally ill are not "us" but "them." This splitting of "us" and "them" weighed more heavily on me as I started thinking about what I wanted to do with my life.

As an adolescent, entrenched in my own art making, one patient in particular fascinated me. He walked the state hospital grounds with huge pieces of poster board on which were detailed drawings. He would sell the drawings to the doctors and whoever would buy them for a dollar or two. The money enabled him to buy more Sharpies and poster board so he could continue to create.

From my understanding of the importance of the creative drive to that patient, along with my understanding of the "us" and "them" mentality of the larger community, it became a desire of mine to make a difference through working with people in a different way than the state hospital did. My emerging identity informed my decision to become an art therapist.

An additional side effect of growing up in that environment was my desire to work with marginalized populations because I was a minority within a homogenous East Coast community. I understood what it felt like to be a token Asian in White society in rural Pennsylvania.

My art therapy identity was a fit for me early on and has remained with me throughout my life. Despite choosing to pursue a doctorate in Marriage and Family Systems, art therapy has always been a compelling and stable force in my identity.

Should the Art Therapy Field Have a Unitary Identity?

I believe that art therapy in its practice is diverse and that people who are art therapists for long periods of time have already established an identity. To me, our art therapy field has morphed into a system where people commonly become Registered Art Therapists,[1] but also need a license that is accepted within each state by a particular licensing board and by health insurance panels. Without a license, art ther-

---

1. Having met certain criteria, an art therapist can become "Registered" (ATR). Originally, "Registration" was granted by the AATA. "Registration" is currently managed by the ATCB, which is separate from the AATA.

apists may not be able to find employment and practice. This economic necessity has certainly presented some unique challenges for the profession and its identity as a whole.

When I entered the profession, it seemed there was an abundance of money in the system—I thought there was more money in the mental health system than we knew what to do with, and as far as I knew, identity problems were not even present. In that era, people like me got a degree in art therapy, but a license was less necessary in most states. I wonder whether it is as much of an identity problem as it is an economic problem? When people need to make hard fiscal choices, is it more reasonable to seek out the license first as opposed to the Registration as an art therapist? That may depend on whatever work situation people have. Faced with fiscal problems, an art therapist may need to morph into different areas, but is art therapy identity really impacted? This is the question.

I believe the image of the umbrella of art therapy identity[2] is multifaceted; currently, because of licensing, more people have multi-identities professionally, but I don't know whether that is different from how one identifies anyway. Any one of us could identify with more than one identity. My identities might include mother, sister, daughter, educator, colleague, brunette, and so on; I think that we can hold several identities at once and not necessarily feel that one has to get lost within the other.

I think an umbrella model for art therapy tends to indicate an all or nothing, often with a message that "you've lost your soul to become licensed." It can be a parallel process to a lot of the duality we have seen in the art therapy profession as a whole. In my opinion, it would be in our best interest in art therapy to stop polarizing whatever is the hot issue or topic of the time. We started out with the polarized Naumberg versus Kramer—art psychotherapy versus art as therapy—and more recently, this polarization has morphed into the art therapy versus license duality. I believe that art therapy can mature as a profession by simultaneously holding several of these identities in hand together.

Art therapy started out as an adjunct therapy off the tails of occupational and recreational therapy and then moved into more of a mental health model framework. Some in the art therapy field criticized

---

2. The "umbrella" is the image that the art therapy profession presents to the "outside" world and to other mental health disciplines.

this model as a medical model without much art. Should art therapy be defined as a mental health discipline? Absolutely! But I don't think that is the only way it could be defined.

Definitions of Art Therapy Identity

Of course, art therapy identity should be within mental health disciplines, but it could be within other disciplines as well. It is utilized within so many different settings and with such differing populations that I hate it to be so reductionist. I think art therapy could also place itself within other non-mental health disciplines. The professional organization for art therapy, the AATA, of course, has also changed over the decades, and I think at times it has helped to clarify and at times confuse art therapy identity.

One of the things that would be interesting to look at is the stabilization of AATA membership over the decades of its existence. Is the membership growing or decreasing? What is it due to and what does it mean? Given the number of art therapy educational programs that have emerged over the years and the number of students graduated, it seems to me that there should have been an upward trajectory in the membership.

I believe part of the way to help move the profession forward is for the AATA to make art therapy attractive and inviting, especially to students when they are in graduate school. The AATA has made some moves in that direction, but for a long time, I do not think they have been competitive with some of the other mental health professions such as the American Counseling Association (ACA) or the American Association for Marriage and Family Therapists (AAMFT). Often the result is that "poor" students who can spend only $30 and who join the ACA (because they may be also studying counseling) may choose not to spend another $120 to join as a student member of the AATA.

It seems to me that there has been some positive movement toward the AATA making membership more accessible and affordable for students, but to me, during their student years is when the AATA should be welcoming and getting them to become members. When students join early and start going to conferences early, it becomes part of their art therapy identity and is something that they become committed to, as opposed to students who do not get into the system early.

Should Art Therapists be "Welcoming" and Inclusive of Others?

Whether we are art therapist clinicians or educators, I feel it is our responsibility as professionals to be welcoming to others who are interested in art and the field. There has been a kind of exclusivity by art therapists, and I think that has been a disadvantage to the field. Because of wanting to retain our uniqueness, we have not been particularly welcoming to other professionals who may want to learn and become part of the art therapy community. That being said, the caution that so many art therapy professionals have about untrained people presenting themselves as art therapists is understandable. In publications such as the *Journal of Marriage and Family Therapy,* mental health professionals are calling what they do "art therapy," when it isn't.

Recently, I encountered an example of this: I was reviewing an article for publication in a non-art therapy journal, and the authors called themselves "art therapists." I contacted them to find out where they had trained. Although they claimed to be art therapists, I discovered they had only attended a weekend workshop. My ears and eyes perked up; I got in touch with the author in the first place because the article contained the names of well-known art therapist authors, whom all art therapy students would have heard of. These names were wrongly spelled. Obviously, this article had made it through reviewers who were not art therapists. The article on doing art therapy later became published in a journal that was difficult to be published in, so I understand the caution. Nonetheless, I believe that there can be room within the profession to welcome others. There does not need to be, as I mentioned before an "us versus them" mentality.

Global Awareness and Art Therapy

One of the exciting opportunities to help art therapy grow and achieve more credibility is to move the profession *globally.* We must not just consider expanding within the United States, where the visibility of art therapy has grown immensely over the years; we need now to think globally. Art therapy in the United States is a leader in education, training, and clinical work and often is far ahead of countries in which it may be only beginning. I believe American art therapy must be inclusive and move toward a truly global community. To me this is one of the most exciting visions: to move the profession forward in a way that can support professionals and those who seek services in art therapy all over the world.

WHY ART THERAPISTS MUST MAKE ART, SELECTIONS AND ADAPTATIONS FROM THE UNPUBLISHED PAPERS OF DON JONES

Don Jones, ATR-BC, HLM, and Karen Rush Jones, MA, ATR-BC

The idea of art as the center of our practice is a simple one. It is what all humans do at times out of neuro-biological necessity. My longstanding philosophy has been that, "In the beginning art was made to overcome chaos." In the best and worst of times, the arts have been the most universal channel for the expressions of both the awesome and the awful. It has been a container for the wounded heart in deepest despair and grief. Art therapy was cloned from the arts. The twin parallel processes are identical, whether used in healing clients or making people aesthetically "Weller than well."

Art as our center is a process qualitatively different from mental health counseling training or skill. My biased concern is the diminishing identity of art therapy, as a discipline in itself, and its being absorbed into practice within the boundaries and requirements of social work and counseling. Will prospective new students go directly to counseling and skip art therapy? Or will training programs slight the art therapy components in favor of counseling courses? Or will students go directly to do art in the community without going to the time and expense of art therapy credentialing. Many groups (clinically qualified or not) are replacing the role and functions of art therapy in educational and social/cultural settings. Art therapy does not own art. So the question remains, Who Are We?

I have always had an umbilical attachment to the art world. It has been my personal, natural coping connection. It is the source of my identity and the basis of my professional activity. Being an artist is the rationale for our encouraging this special effort of connecting art therapy with the art world and with the culture. Aesthetic experiences are to be found in affective-emotional expressions, and contemporary aesthetics need not be primarily cognitive, rationally minimalist, or objectively analytical.

Why must art therapists engage continuously in arts activity? One might ask why we even need to pose this question. Basically, it [making art] is to educate our expressive natures and to sharpen our nonverbal clinical communication skills. It is a matter of enhancing professional competence. Art making is a personal process of self-discovery and introspection, a way to explore and understand the deep places in ourselves and our clients. The imagination stretches, touches, and is reacquainted with those deeper sources of being human. Ongoing engagement in art expression is an essential part of our vocation and continuing personal and professional identity. Art is our way of growing in self-awareness and insight, personally and as therapists. It is the tool for understanding our clients. We can find inspiration and ever new and changing dynamic in our work. It is dishonest to ask our clients to do anything that we have not or will not do or are not doing ourselves.

Doing the "work" of art is both a personal and professional issue of survival. Were you to live as an alien in a foreign country for 25 years, would you hope to learn and be expected to speak the language? The extensive uses of imagery and metaphor in everyday interactions and clinical practice imply that art expressions "speak" mysteriously different, in a wordless right hemisphere dialect. The root of our English word *mystery* is a Greek verb *muein*–to close the mouth–that which cannot be talked about, but can be shown, witnessed, revealed, but not explained. (You ask me to speak of the color RED . . . I will say "think, imagine rose, rust of iron, cherry, flamingo, dawn, lips, blood, blush"). The right hemisphere's alphabet is unique, neither like Russian nor Greek, because one hemisphere sings and dances and the other doesn't!

Imagery is not just visual. Images are mental patterns, neurologically designed and recorded as visual, auditory, olfactory, gustatory, somasensory, touch, muscular, temperature and pain, visceral, vestibular. (The sound and feel of the wind.) Sounds like music or acoustic sounds like sighs, shouts, and cries shape and reflect emotions with stunning precision. Image making never stops, awake or asleep. It is a process of spontaneous flow of instantaneous impulse images recorded as chemical and neurological data. This is the energy source and "royal road" of the art impulse. To ignore the power of the arts in healing is like standing on a whale fishing for minnows.

I invite you to think about new ways of using the arts to touch the neuro-sensory-cognitive-emotional wordless areas of pain and resistance hardwired in your clients' being. After all, words are only invented references, and sometimes we use hollow phrases and process words three or four steps removed from the inner struggle. Five hundred years ago, before the printing press was invented, nearly everyone was illiterate. Now, with the new technology, we are hyper-literate, depending on and easily influenced by empty words–words that have eroded the active use of our whole brain, forgetting that one half of our consciousness is imagery! The debate between word and image is not new. Of course, the expressive word, the acoustic word, as singing, shouting, or in verse, has the possibility of echoing emotional recall.

Words such as *difficult, chronic, addiction, yes,* and *alcoholic* are process words used as if they were specific and explicitly describing things. "Chronic" is a category, a ward, even the "chronic staff." Language stunts creativity! Imaging, as well as using words, is rational and cognitive because these are basic functions of the brain and mind. The use of expressive art forms offers the most precise therapeutic tool and may be the only therapeutic approach based directly on neuro-evolutionary processes. However, it is often dismissed because the art form may not be neatly measured by quantitative and statistical means and is about those irrational things that words cannot always explain: laughter, faith, art and beauty, sexual arousal, love at first sight, dance, altruism, patriotism–that lump in the throat from joy or misery. There are implicit images of traumatic events repressed and stored in the memories of those who remain speechless because there are no associated words to assist recall. Only by the skilled applications of "irrational" healing processes and sophisticated methods of "arting-out" can such dramatic scenes be brought directly into consciousness and safely reenacted and defused.

Our left hemispheres have been through a rigorous K-12 education and advanced academic training and discipline, while even those of us who are self-declared practicing artists are probably still somewhere in a K-6 creative learning process, although growing vigorously. Our art therapy field is still in the first generation, and we seem reluctant to use those elementary expressive talents, which have been its origins and energy, trusting more in secondary learned skills.

It is not easy to make time to make art. But along with the urgent demands of daily existence, the process and necessity of creating and doing the "work" of art is our lifeline. The first obvious thing to do to reunite with our twins in the art world is to produce art works! It must be part of our daily work in therapy, teaching, and in our life and leisure.

Anything worth doing takes more than one lifetime, so lean on it! We will be able to heal our philosophical differences and be able to posit a vision of "who we are" but perhaps not yet. We must give ourselves permission and a rationale to continue "tinkering" while seeking to consolidate an art-based professional identity, philosophy, and method. Let us not make our vision "fixed" or rigid. It must allow for inclusion and growth. An organic form will emerge independent from a former strictly medical model, becoming a balanced, equal blending of medicine, holistic health, and the expressive arts. Art is elemental, and the future is hopeful as there is an increasing sensitivity to the necessity of art as an adaptive process.

Perhaps the expressive therapies can concentrate on an alliance of art, music, dance, and drama rather than having to conform to the boundary lines of other therapy disciplines. To conceive of the future is to first look backward and inward, then to envision a goal, next to confront the barriers, and finally to use the perspective to plan strategies for success. And in the meantime, "words" encrypted in the paint, the clay, the poem, the song, and the dance do the "work" of the arts—continuing to transmute feelings into works of art that are both therapeutic and life affirming.

GONE MISSING: A SHARED IDENTITY

Frances F. Kaplan, MPS, DA, ATR-BC

When I started in the field of art therapy, I thought I knew what art therapy was. Now, I'm not so sure. Before I had even begun my studies, my view was that it was a discipline with one foot in art and one foot in science. With refinements, I still hold this view (Kaplan, 2000). To my amazement, I soon discovered that not every member of the profession agreed with me. But before further discussion of this last (I will return to it later), let me clarify my stance by providing some of my personal history.

When I was trying to find out how I might combine my two loves, art and science, I talked to different professors at Florida State University (FSU) where I was working on my undergraduate degree. One suggested that I become a medical illustrator, another that I restore old paintings (therapy for art). Neither of these options appealed. Indeed, it seemed as though I was being directed toward applying the skills of one branch of study to a product of the other. But what I wanted was a combination of the processes of both.

Some years passed. I got married and became pregnant. While I was pregnant and waiting for the baby to arrive, I read about a woman who was doing art with disturbed boys, and I said, "AHA! That sounds like what I've been trying to find." She was an artist, and she said she was going to study sociology to round things out. I had majored in chemistry at FSU and minored in art. I suddenly realized that part of the problem was that I had chosen the wrong science. It was the social and behavioral sciences that were the most appropriate for what I wanted to do, which included being a helper. So I thought, "I'm going to talk some university into letting me combine art and psychology in a graduate degree." Sometime later, I was talking to an artist acquaintance, telling him about what I wanted to study, and he said, "They have that already-at Pratt Institute in Brooklyn."

Thus, I determined to get my master's degree at Pratt. I was living in New Jersey, and Pratt was a hike. Every time I went to Pratt, I would drive to a neighboring town, get on a commuter train to Hoboken, transfer to an underground subway train to the World Trade Center, get off there, and then take two New York City subway trains before finally getting to my destination. The art therapy program at Pratt was one of the first in this or any other country, and I was lucky to live as close as I did. I enrolled my son, now about five, in a school that had day care. Years had passed since I had first gotten the idea to pursue what eventually became my profession, the actual travel was daunting, yet the excitement of taking the metaphorical journey of becoming an art therapist consistently drew me forward.

I loved studying art therapy. I was older than many of the students; however, quite a few students, like myself, had wanted to create such a discipline. We more or less felt as though we had "invented" it until we found out that Margaret Naumburg, Edith Kramer, and the founders of early training programs had gone before us. Now, in the 21st century, high school guidance counselors know about art therapy and steer suitable students in that direction. Then, in the early 1970s, few people knew anything about it. Indeed, when I was at FSU, no one seemed to have an inkling that such thing was in the making.

After I got my master's degree at Pratt, I worked for a while in psychiatric settings. I learned from these work experiences, but I felt I had more studying to do. Serendipitously, I heard there was a new program at New York University (NYU) for people in the arts who had not previously had the opportunity to get a doctorate because none or few suitable doctoral programs existed. Scholarship money came with being accepted to enroll in this program, which was open to studio artists and practitioners of the different creative arts therapies. I jumped at this opportunity, and eight years later, I had my doctorate. (Working part time and taking care of a house and child was part of the reason this was such a drawn-out process.)

Still, during all the time it took to undertake and complete my art therapy training, I never doubted that art therapy was or should be a blend of art and science. I was working at that point at Carrier Foundation—a rather posh psychiatric hospital in Belle Mead, New Jersey. The average stay for patients in the facility was about a month, and because I mainly ran groups rotating through different units in the hospital, I sometimes didn't see a particular patient more than once. Single-session therapy seemed disappointingly ineffective. However, I eventually got a little more continuity in my work because one of the psychiatrists at the hospital agreed to run an ongoing art psychotherapy group with me for his patients. Later, when I left Carrier for another position, he told me that he had learned a lot from me. Certainly, this was gratifying to hear and, looking back, suggests that I was approaching an amalgam of art and science in practice as well as in theory.

From the beginning, I thought of myself as doing art psychotherapy. Over the years, I have developed a more precise definition of the *art* and *science* involved. Art therapy as a profession is an amalgam, but the profession hasn't been as well developed along these lines as it could be. For me, *art* means producing something that is both personally meaningful and has some degree of aesthetic appeal. Here's an example: I get frequent blood tests to check up on certain medical conditions that plague me. Recently, I was chatting with my regular phlebotomist and discovered that she is a "weekend" artist. She showed me an album with photos of her work. Much of it was decorative, but one painting stood out. It represented her feelings about losing her home after what was apparently a messy divorce. The painting showed a large shovel digging up a piece of landscape with a house on it. The painting was appealing in formal terms as well as highly evocative. She said the image appeared to her when the divorce was settled. She also referred to her artwork as her fun and her therapy.

When I talk about the *science* aspect of the amalgam, I mean that research in art therapy and the social and behavioral sciences is involved and very much needs to be taken into account if art therapists want to help people in the best way. There has been too little emphasis on doing research in the field and in following the research done by related professionals. I am happy to say that this is slowly changing, but the road ahead is still long. Further, it needs to be traveled with care; there is much that has been applied to therapy that is either pseudoscience or based on research that is poorly done. There seems to be a feeling among the rank and file of our profession that anything that has been published is valid and valid forever more. This is not the way for a solid profession to progress.

I will return now to the statement above that not all art therapists think of the profession as encompassing art and science. Setting aside those who have entered the field as a way of making a living using art, let us consider those who remain. These are the art therapists and related professionals who see *art therapy* as a form of "magic." I do not believe that art therapy implies spiritual (a vague term) or religious underpinnings. Moreover, I do not believe that some sort of universal or quasi-Freudian or Jungian understanding of symbols should be part of the process—as a sizable number of art therapists still seem to do. Indeed, much of what had been considered valid in this area is disputed by relatively recent research (Gantt & Tabone, 1998; Smith & Dumont, 1995.) There is sufficient evidence in the real world of everyday existence to no longer need such justifications, and further research should uncover more (Slayton, D'Archer, & Kaplan, 2010.)

Much of the writing in art therapy has been casework and how to do art therapy in different ways and with different populations. But it is well past time for art therapists to think and write more cogently about ideas leading to well-formed theory. The literature needs to move past what it can do into an art-psychological universe of ideas. We are in real danger of our most curious art therapy students and practitioners being led down the garden path by outmoded and erroneous thinking.

Psychotherapy is trying to help people through language, and using imagery as well as words extends this language. When I go back to my hometown in Florida, and I say I've become an art therapist, they respond, "Art what?" I then reply, "A psychotherapist who uses art in therapy." By claiming to be a psychotherapist, I do not mean one way of being, but I do mean being psychologically minded. I had a psychoanalytically trained teacher at NYU whom I highly respected; interestingly, he practiced as a teacher and researcher, not as a psychotherapist. However, he knew from scientific evidence whereof he spoke. He emphasized that the Rogerian therapeutic behaviors of empathy, unconditional positive regard, warmness, and so on were necessary but not sufficient for effective therapy (Holt, 1989). I submit that including the production of certain kinds of artistic imagery is one way to provide an additional part that leads to sufficiency. Art can make the process deeper, more expansive, and more profound. Plenty of art therapists use art but do not know about the therapeutic process as a whole. Simply making a piece of art for personal enjoyment or for art's sake is not the most effective way to proceed.

Unfortunately, our professional organization, the American Art Therapy Association has never jelled in a helpful way. Things seem to change direction at whim, and there has been little historical continuity. A new president and a new executive director come in, along with staff, to handle the day-to-day operations, who may not fully understand art therapy. Thus, we remain a field of practice without a firm theoretical base or an organization we can count on. If art therapists are to have a meaningful professional association, this must change.

In summary, my art therapy identity and that of the profession as a whole do not match. One could even say that the latter does not have an identity but simply depends on whom one talks to. The question I then ask myself is, "Am I a person without a profession or a member of a profession reluctant to progress?" If art therapy is to survive as a separate vocation, this issue must be dealt with, but I begin to fear that it will not happen in my lifetime—if at all.

References

Gantt, L., & Tabone, C. (1998). *The format elements art therapy scale: The rating manual.* Morgantown, WV: Gargoyle Press.

Holt, R. (1989). *Freud reappraised: A fresh look at psychoanalytic theory.* New York: Guilford Press.

Kaplan, F. (2000). *Art, science and art therapy: Repainting the picture.* London, England: Jessica Kingsley.

Slayton, S., D'Archer, J., & Kaplan, F. (2010). Outcome studies on the efficacy of art therapy: A review of findings. *Art Therapy: Journal of the American Art Therapy Association, 2*(3), 108–119.

Smith, D., & Dumont, F. (1995). A cautionary study: Unwarranted interpretations of the Draw-A-Person Test. *Professional Psychology: Research and Practice, 2*(3), 298–303.

TO DUAL OR NOT TO DUAL

Myra F. Levick, PhD, ATR-BC, HLM

When I received the invitation from Dr. Maxine Junge to contribute to her book, I was honored and grateful that an esteemed colleague was providing a platform for discussion of what I consider a most critical issue for the future of art therapy and art therapists. Dr. Junge offered questions to possibly use as a guide in preparing this response. As I reviewed these questions, I found myself in a déjà vu experience.

It was 1994, and the 25th anniversary of the American Art Therapy Association was approaching. Cathy Malchiodi, the editor of *Art Therapy, Journal of the American Art Therapy Association,* announced a special 25th anniversary section of that journal and invited several past officers of the organization and pioneer art therapists to write an essay. I was one of those invited and, prompted by Dr. Junge's questions, began to reread what I had written many years ago.

I noted Dr. Malchiodi had also provided questions: "How will the profession of art therapy change in the next 25 years?" she asked. "What is your vision of the 21st century art therapist?" While I was pleased to be given that opportunity, back then I realized that for me those questions evoked more questions (Levick 1994). I wrote then, "I consider it nearly impossible to even suggest how the profession will change over the next quarter of a century. And the vision I have for the next century, at this point, remains a wish" (Levick, 1994, p. 98).

My essay for the 25th anniversary journal addressed the training of the art therapist at that time and how it impacted the role of the art therapist in the field of mental health in 1994 and in the future (Levick, 1994). Maintaining high standards of education and practice had been embraced by the professional membership of the AATA. The requirement of a master's degree in art therapy for professional membership was adopted and a Credentials Board was working toward national certification (Levick, 1978, 1989, 1994). However, there was a problem: AATA-"Approved" art therapy educational programs met established criteria in the areas of curriculum and clinical hours, but I wrote: "There is no consistency—we do not speak the same language" (Levick, 1994, p. 98).

To make my point, I described my confrontation in 1996 when I was invited by Janet Bush, director of the Clinical Art Therapy program at Miami-Dade (Florida) School System, to develop a single art therapy assessment to be used by 11 art therapists employed at that time. I was informed that within the 11 art therapists, there were five different art therapy/psychology assessments being used to communicate diagnosis, treatment goals and progress to school counselors, teachers, and other school staff for this special needs population. This project is discussed in detail in another paper (Levick, 1989), and below are my brief comments in that journal essay:

> Janet was charged with developing an art therapy evaluation instrument for the 11 art therapists on her staff. She engaged me as the consultant to this project, using my work on cognitive and emotional indicators manifested in children's drawings as a basis for what is now known as the *Levick Emotional & Cognitive Art Therapy Assessment* (Levick, 1989). It was only a few short months before we realized that to move forward, we needed to retreat and teach the theoretical construct only a few were even a little familiar with. That three-year process, in no small measure revealed the inconsistency and fragmentation of our art therapy educational system. The positive outcome was that we emerged as a small cadre of highly trained art therapists, not only able to speak the same language, but also able to communicate this knowledge to colleagues from different disciplines in the school system. (Levick, 1994, pp. 98 & 99)

This assessment has been revised and normed and continues to be an integral part of that program, which now employs 20 art therapists (Levick, 2009). I titled that paper "To Be or Not to Be."

Now, 18 years later, I read Dr. Junge's questions and shudder at the realization that nothing much has changed. In fact the inconsistency and fragmentation have expanded, and art therapy is overrun with dual degrees and multiple identities.

To focus my responses here and help me refrain from ranting and raving, I will try to address those questions I think are most relevant to the identity of the art therapist. Dr. Junge asks if we think art therapy "could benefit from a stable, unitary identity"? I ask, how could it not? Every other mental health professional has a single identity–psychologists are psychologists regardless of whether they practice clinical psychology, forensic psychology, school psychology, and so on. The same is true for psychiatrists, occupational therapists, mental health counselors, dance therapists, and music therapists. Being different kinds of therapists, subscribing to different professional identities, is confusing to the community we serve and undermines the professional discipline of art therapy.

In 1994, I expressed concern that the credibility of art therapy was burdened with the many definitions created by the different orientations approved by AATA's education standards committee. This burden has not lessened. It has been compounded by a number of "Approved" graduate programs that offer a dual degree—art therapy and counseling or another mental health discipline. Most recently, I was appalled to see that a second-year student graduating from a program that did not offer a dual degree, in her profile for the program, added "mental health counselor" to her art therapy degree. Knowing the school she was graduating from, I questioned this altering of her degree. The answer was cavalier. She told me she knows the school does not offer a dual degree, but she "intends to do it all." How unfortunate for her and for the field. *Hutzpah* and a dual identity do not make a professional art therapist.

Dr. Junge asked us to respond to other dualities. One is the age-old difference between the art therapy models put forth by Naumburg (1966) and Kramer (1958). For me this was never a duality but two parts of a whole. In the graduate program I founded at Hahnemann Medical College and Hospital 1967 (now Drexel University), our curriculum was defined first by psychodynamic theory and Naumburg's approach to art therapy, followed by Kramer's approach, which does not invite patients to make associations or interpretations of their art work. What was paramount in this curriculum was to understand the needs of the patient, establish treatment goals, and work to meet those goals through art therapy using Naumburg, Kramer, or both. I believe this is still the core of the core curriculum in art therapy in this program.

This brief discussion of the duality in art therapy theory provides a segue for me to speak to concerns that some of my colleagues may have identifying art therapy with anything close to the medical model and/or defining it as a mental health profession.

It is clear, from the writings of our early pioneers (Kramer, 1958; Kwiatkowska, 1962; Naumburg, 1966; Ulman & Dachinger 1975) that the populations for whom they were providing art therapy were "patients"—children, adults, families, and groups that were diagnosed with some form of emotional and/or cognitive impairment. These pioneers were *mental health care givers* regardless of whether their patients were in a hospital setting, a school for children with special needs, or a facility such as the National Institute of Mental Health. With the establishment of standards for education on a graduate level and the formation of the American Art Therapy Association, we became *mental health professionals,* and art therapy became a mental health discipline. In my view, an art therapy program or art therapist who does not accept this identity is not following the definition of art therapy as stated in our earliest and subsequent mission statements. There is no place for multiple definitions of art therapy and for multiple identities. They impede our ability to lobby for licensing and impact our credibility as a profession.

Relevant to this is the major issue of our professional association, AATA, wanting to include other professionals in our organization and another issue that supports teaching other professionals how to do art therapy. Over the years, AATA officers have suggested we include other mental health professionals in our membership. I and others have objected strongly to this inclusion of any mental health professional who does not have art therapy credentials. I know of no other health organization that offers membership to anyone not credentialed in the discipline of that organization.

There are those who support "teaching" other mental health professionals to use art in their private practice and say they are doing art therapy. As an art therapy community, we cannot support this, and wherever we can, we must discourage it. We must be clear about our identity and maintain our integrity. To emphasize my point here, I offer a personal vignette. In 1976, Pennsylvania established a psychology license and grandparented in anyone with a master's degree in Psychology. I had an MEd in Adolescent Psychology from Temple University, and the chairman of my department at Hahnemann Medical College insisted I apply for this license so the department could be reimbursed for whatever patients I was referred. I did apply, was awarded the license, and became a member of the Pennsylvania Psychology Association and the American Psychology Association. My practice, listed in the directories of these two associations, was Art Psychotherapy. This listing was repeated in every subsequent published directory. I retired my license in 2000, but I am listed as a "retired" member who practiced Art Psychotherapy of both organizations.

Unfortunately, the AATA has not been a stable organization over the past 43 years, and AATA leadership has naturally represented the different definitions of art therapy regardless of the mission statement. Likewise, the different orientations of "Approved"[1] programs have influenced the directions elected leaders have taken in moving our profession forward. There have been instances when leadership assumed an Executive Director and office staff could steer our ship. Consequently, as a result of these conflicting definitions and orientations and office staff who may have a good knowledge of business but not art therapy, we have had a bumpy ride that has taken us in different directions sideways instead of upward and forward.

As an organization, the AATA has allowed other mental health professionals to use art activities and say they are doing art therapy. As an organization, we have submitted to calling ourselves something else in order to get a license to practice. We rationalize that this is okay, because we continue to practice art therapy—not whatever the particular license may specify. I acknowledge I did the same thing, albeit not by choice. The difference is that I was able to publish and preserve my professional identity. I also acknowledge that as an educator in our field, I had more experience and credibility than an art therapist who has just completed graduate studies.

We now have AATA-"Approved" programs offering a dual degree in art therapy and counseling (or another mental health profession). I can understand the anxiety and need to be licensed to obtain employment and, in some states, to be eligible for third-party health insurance payments. We know this varies from state to state, creating an enormous obstacle to art therapy's growth. This is another issue that I believe our organization has not put forth the necessary effort to address: Compromising, diluting, and/or giving up our professional identity is not okay. There are other ways to be remunerated for our expertise and better maintain our identity as art therapists.

As an example, I share my work experience over the past 25 years. I have been living in Florida since 1986 and have been employed and

---

1. AATA assesses applying programs according to its Educational Standards and issues "Approval." Program "Approval" is AATA's form of accreditation.

practiced art psychotherapy these many years without obtaining a license. I knew beforehand that this state is not reciprocal in licensing professionals in the medical field, and my Pennsylvania psychology license would not be accepted here–if I chose to go that route. Therefore, it was my responsibility to learn what my options were in order for me to continue to be a practicing art therapist in Florida. I learned in this state that a mental health therapist, regardless of discipline employed in a licensed facility, does not need a license. As an employee in an in-patient rehabilitation facility for dual-diagnosed substance abusers, I was not required to be licensed. I worked there for 12 years, retired, and was replaced by another art therapist who does not have a license. The same was true for employment in a facility for Alzheimer's patients and another in a psychiatric hospital in Palm Beach County. For years I worked with private patients, doing art psychotherapy as a contract art therapist to psychiatrists and psychologists. Given the vituperative turf protection in this state, I was called before the License Bureau and Grievance Board demanding I apply for a Mental Health Counselor's license. Fortunately, as stated above, I knew the state laws, and as an employee and a contract person, I did not need a license. Directors of both agencies were required to apologize to me and send a copy of the transcript of my hearing and a written letter of apology. It was a victory for me but a hollow one for our field. This should not have to be the only way to survive. Until we are able to obtain licensing for art therapists, it is our responsibility to learn the laws of the state we are living in regarding employment and/or private practice and define how to work within those laws (or, perhaps, how to work around them).

In my view, there is yet a greater obstacle to our growth and credibility: Art therapy has been failed by our early leaders who established education standards embracing different orientations. I include myself in what I now know to be a serious mistake. We have shot ourselves in the foot by embracing the notion that it is okay to get a license in another discipline as long as we practice art therapy. There are now Approved programs that offer a degree in art therapy and counseling. These programs include counseling courses in their curriculum to ensure their students' ability to qualify for a mental health counseling license. I realize the rationale behind these decisions is based on the fact that art therapists throughout the country have had difficulty obtaining employment. Obviously turf battles have contributed to this, in addition, art therapy is a convoluted discipline that preaches different orientations in graduate education, different approaches to practice, and no basic curriculum for all graduate education. This is totally different than our fellow mental health professionals, who must study the same core curriculum before taking courses in a specific sub-specialty of their field. I see us in the process of being subsumed by the American Counseling Association by the offering of dual degrees in art therapy and counseling and by other disciplines to which we offer art therapy courses in seminars and workshops without requiring graduate matriculation.

How can we stop this downhill ride? I have learned recently that the AATA is working to obtain an art therapy classification in the Department of Labor. If we achieve that, we have much to do to maintain it, including the need to endorse a core curriculum that includes recognized and respected diverse art therapy theories and major developmental theoretical constructs. We will need a core curriculum that teaches and demands evidenced-based art therapy in all Approved programs. We must galvanize state art therapy chapters to work with each other to lobby for art therapy licensing; we must be sure our office staff are informed and supervised to do whatever possible to support these efforts and be more proactive in challenging other mental health professionals who claim they do art therapy. We must stop supporting dual degrees that lead to dual identities.

As a practicing art psychotherapist for almost 50 years, I never cease to be in awe of what emerges in an art therapy session. Art therapy is a unique and amazing discipline that was labeled "the x-ray of the brain" by one of my mentors. We must work together to secure one identity—Art Therapy.

References

Kramer, E. (1958). *Art therapy in a children's community*. Springfield, IL: Charles C Thomas.

Kwiatkowska, H. (1962). Family evaluation: Experiments with a new technique. *Bulletin of Art Therapy, (1)*, 3–15.

Levick, M. (1978). Summary of panel presentations: American Art Therapy Conference. *Art Psychotherapy, An International Journal, (5)*, 3–4.

Levick, M. (1983). *They could not talk and so they drew: Children's styles of coping and thinking*. Springfield, IL: Charles C Thomas.

Levick, M. (1989). Reflections: On the road to educating the creative arts therapist. *The Arts in Psychotherapy.*

Levick, M. (1994). Perspective: To be or not to be. *Art Therapy, Journal of the American Art Therapy Association, (11)*, 97–100.

Levick, M. (2009). *Levick emotional and cognitive art therapy assessment: A normative study.* Bloomington, IN: AuthorHouse.

Naumburg, M. (1966). *Dynamically oriented art therapy: Its principles and practice.* New York: Grune & Stratton. [Reprinted in 1987, Chicago, IL: Magnolia Street.]

Ulman, E., & Dachinger, P. (Eds.). (1975). *Art therapy in theory and practice.* New York: Schocken.

FINDING MY VOICE

Debra Linesch, PhD, MFT, ATR-BC

Whatever is at the core of being an art therapist organized itself pretty early for me; now I call it "finding my voice." I always defaulted to making things as a kid as a way of surviving/thriving in my family. There was little support for the arts but encouragement for trying new things. Somehow I came to know the art process as a way of accessing and understanding my internal experiences. I was an introverted, introspective, and creative child. As a young woman, I studied painting and, after losing my father, began the first of several serious psychotherapy endeavors and four years of psychoanalysis. It was a concerted and tenacious attempt to continue finding my voice, a goal that dominated my life. In what turned out to be a wonderful coincidence, the simultaneity of my most extended painting exploration and my deepest personal psychotherapy exploration facilitated powerful awareness and self-knowledge. After college I started out as a first grade teacher. I had a class full of six-year-old recent immigrants-and all that seemed important to do with them were art projects. They were kids so impacted by poverty, immigration experiences, and acculturation challenges that the first-grade curriculum seemed much less valuable than encouraging them to find out who they were by engaging in creative explorations. Then I found out that there was something called art therapy, and it brought everything together. Still studying painting and continuing in psychoanalysis, I started looking for art therapy programs and ultimately came to Los Angeles for the master's program at Immaculate Heart College. The program's focus was *clinical* art therapy.

Becoming a clinical art therapist wasn't something I had sought out at first, but I took to it extraordinarily well and loved it for a long time. I like to think I have contributed to the practice of clinical art therapy by writing, teaching, and presenting. I dove fully into the clinical practice and wrote two books, *Adolescent Art Therapy* and *Art Therapy with Families in Crisis* (1988, 1993). This way of practicing was based on a serious commitment to the centrality of the art process within traditional psychotherapeutic models. But I believe that my identity as a clinical art therapist in truth was a *smaller* identity within the more expansive identity of a person committed to the healing potential of the creative process. For example, I have always loved doing the kind of work I currently support at Dolores Mission in East Los Angeles-studio-based art therapy. And I just spent the last three years studying Torah as an art therapy project and wrote a book about it–*Midrashic Mirrors: Creating Holiness in Imagery and Intimacy* (2013). This art therapy venture into the most personal of lived experiences–my struggle to find meaningful spiritual practices–represents my most recent expansion of the boundary of my identity as an art therapist. As I articulate in the Introduction to the book, "Although I believe that artistic expression enhances knowing and meaning, I was unsure whether my own yearnings for deeper connections to the Torah would be satisfied by this exploration." This book, like many things in my life, represents the core of my identity and my belief in creativity, in which the identity of clinical art therapist was just one aspect. Clinical art therapy was my identity for a long time, but there was always a larger identity containing that practice. I am someone who believes in the healing power of art in all areas of life. Everything I've done in my life has been based on that central belief.

I learned how to be a good clinician who centralized the art within the psychotherapy process. I was quite happy doing that and felt empowered particularly when I was working with severely disturbed kids. I look back to those early years of my professional development and think I was so lucky to have met those kids and to have had the art as a way to work with them. I do truly believe in the process. As I'm nearing retirement, I'm talking now about building a studio in the garage-the next renovation project. In some as of yet undetermined way, I would like women to come there and work on finding their voices. Right now I'm exploring and pushing out the boundaries of my professional identity.

I've never cared about the dichotomous labels of art psychotherapy/art in therapy. I saw them as distracting and ridiculous. Sometimes I'm not even sure there is a field called art therapy–perhaps this label is just another creator of arbitrary boundaries around processes that are complex, multi-layered, and difficult to categorize. Over the years, I have observed art therapists who use art in ways that miss the opportunity to harness the creative healing potential, and I have observed psychotherapists who, although untrained in official art therapy practices, facilitate deep engagement with creative processes. The label "art

therapy" sometimes implies an artificial boundary and makes something that can and should be so dynamic very static. I guess I'm questioning all these boundaries, rules, and definitions that seem to have
become part of the profession, even though I probably contributed to
some of them.

I am often asked, do you need to be an artist to be an art therapist?
Or keep doing your own art? That question is complex. I know people who are so involved in their art practice that it makes being an art
therapist difficult for them. I think to be helpful to another person, you
have to struggle to keep the creative process going in your own life,
but that's in everything, not just in art. I believe you must constantly
work to access your inner voice, lived through the creative process.
When interviewing applicants for the master's program at Loyola
Marymount University, I look for people who have transformed inner
experience into awareness or external understanding and know what
that's about. So I don't think you need to be a trained and practicing
artist, but you have to be involved in some sort of creative process in
an ongoing way. It is almost alchemy– taking inner experience and
making it into an outer awareness. You have to have touched, and continue to touch, that deep and good place within yourself.

Additionally, I think I have learned most about what it means to be
an art therapist from my experiences as a parent. As the mother of two
now grown adults, I was always aware of how privileged I was to contribute to and observe human development so intimately. I know now
that, because of my commitment to externalizing internal experiences
through creative endeavors, my children were constantly exposed to
opportunities to express themselves, in all ways and forms. Because my
own development as an art therapist coincided with the maturation of
my children, it is hard for me to separate the observations that spilled
over between those two lived roles. My third book, *Celebrating Family
Milestones by Making Art Together* (2000), is a reflection of the way this
identity penetrated everything I did as a parent.

So it seems to me, as I reflect on the question of art therapy identity, that after more than 30 years of practicing as an art therapist, the
core values that make up my professional identity have more to do
with an expansive belief in the meaning-making potential of the artistic process. This belief has pervaded everything I have done, from my
professional life to my personal life and even reaching deep into my

spiritual yearnings. Perhaps there is no field called art therapy, perhaps there is no practice called art therapy, and perhaps there is no job title called art therapist. Rather there is a way of approaching life–parenting, teaching, psychotherapy, religious tradition, everything–that values and embraces creative processes as enhancing, deepening, and growth facilitating. My observation is that the field of art therapy, in which I have long positioned myself, has erroneously struggled to define itself in a historic series of dichotomies rather than open itself to an expansive and inclusive set of ideas.

References

Linesch, D. (1988). *Adolescent art therapy.* New York: Routledge.

Linesch, D. (1993). *Art therapy with families in crisis.* New York: Brunner/Mazel.

Linesch, D. (2000). *Celebrating family milestones.* Ontario, Canada & New York: Firefly Books.

Linesch, D. (2013). *Midrashic Mirrors: Creating holiness in imagery and intimacy.* Self-published, available at www.midrashicmirrors.org.

TO BE OR NOT TO BE? THAT IS NO LONGER THE QUESTION

Mercedes B. ter Maat, PhD, LPC, ATR-BC

Note: This essay is essentially a position statement by the president of American Art Therapy Association (the major professional organization for art therapy) about AATA's current philosophy and policies. While this is not predominantly a statement of an art therapist's views about her own and the profession's identity, as are the other essays in this book, I have decided to print it here anyway as a useful indication of where the president of AATA sees art therapy today. First, Dr. ter Maat addresses the ongoing rumor that the Association is making plans to become part of the American Counseling Association–a prevalent concern expressed by many of a dual or lost identity for the profession of art therapy. –MBJ

For nearly four years, since I have been president of the AATA, not a single discussion, proposal, or communication has taken place about AATA working with the ACA. I cannot speak for any other art therapy or creative arts therapies group, but it is upsetting to know that unfounded rumors continue to exist. I understand that there may be a historical mistrust of AATA and as a result, conspiracy theories tend to take on a life of their own. Perhaps rumors are generated by the uninformed or uninvolved, those who do not peruse the Association website or read written communications (e.g., monthly membership e-blasts, quarterly member Newsletters, quarterly Chapter updates, quarterly Educator's updates), those who do not attend our conferences, or simply by those who prefer to live in the past and choose to perpetuate negativity, conflict, and damaging rumors in the face of what seems to be an obvious reality. I find it interesting that none of these rumors has reached me directly: I have not received one email from an individual, member or not, questioning or stating that the AATA is collaborating with the ACA to end the profession of art therapy as we know it. Moreover, nowhere in the Association's literature since I have been in an elected position (2009) exists communication of collaboration, unofficially or officially, with counseling or other associations. By written communication, I mean Board of Director's meeting minutes, motions carried or denied, committee meeting minutes, and minutes from annual business meetings held at the conference [of the AATA].

Several years ago, and for a short period of time in its history, the AATA *was* managed by the American Counseling Association. Perhaps here is where these rumors were born. The AATA has no intention to align, reconnect, merge, or be managed by the ACA or its Creativity in Counseling subdivision. I have written and will continue to write letters to the Editor of *Counseling Today,* an ACA publication, to educate its readers and voice outrage at the articles that continue to be published implying that counselors can add art, music, dance, and other creative expressions into their practice without the proper training or credentials. I cannot speak for the intentions of ACA, but I can speak for the intentions of the AATA—and there are none to become "art therapy counseling."

Neither art therapists nor the AATA have control over how mental health professionals practice or use art in clinical settings, but the notion that the skills of a mental health worker with some art supplies are equivalent to those of an educated, trained, and credentialed art therapist is preposterous. It is no mistake that the mandated time for art therapy master's-level education is a minimum of two calendar years. There is a lot to learn, a good deal of depth and complexity to the combined knowledge and supervised experience with art media, the creative process, art therapy technique, developmental theory, and psychology. To imply or recommend that to simply employ art in practice is a disservice to art therapists, to art therapy educational standards, and to the profession. It is also a disservice to consumers and a violation of ethical codes—using techniques outside of one's area of training and level of expertise. Such violations are sanctioned by both the Association's Ethical Principles for Art Therapists (American Art Therapy Association, 2011) and ACA's Code of Ethics (American Counseling Association, 2005). Trained and experienced art therapists have much to offer to other mental health professionals; they are usually eager and delighted to act as consultants, colleagues, and co-therapists to safeguard client welfare.

As to my professional identity, I received a master's degree in art therapy from the George Washington University and practiced art therapy for 14 years before I obtained a master's in counseling to be able to keep my position in the schools of Arlington County, Virginia. I am, first and foremost, an art therapist with an additional degree in counseling. But throughout the years and due to my positions as full-time professor in Counselor Education programs, I developed a dual identity as an art therapist and a counselor/counselor educator. Duality is not foreign to me. Having been born and raised in Argentina but living in the United States for the past 30+ years, I am living proof of the successful merge of two opposite worlds. I am bicultural and bilingual, and I am an art therapist, a counselor, and a counselor educator. I can be all without having to give up one for the other, or join a "melting pot." The adoption of an art therapy and counseling identity was much easier and less emotionally charged than my acculturation experience–but with work and conscious determination at the end, I can be true to both ends of the duality without fearing betrayal, embarrassment, shame, criticism, or selling out. I am richer for being a bicultural and bilingual individual; I am richer and more skilled for being an art therapist and counselor scholar-practitioner.

Because I am not an art therapy educator, I cannot speak to how educational programs instruct candidates in the development of an art therapy or dual identity (e.g., art therapy and marriage and family therapist, counselor, psychologist, etc.). Some art therapy master's programs have, since their inception, been called something other than art therapy to fulfill the licensure and labor requirements of mental health workers in a particular state. Those necessities of the marketplace continue today, and therefore some art therapy programs are starting or continue to offer dual degrees to open employability doors and arm art therapy graduates with as many tools as possible. As president of the AATA, I am familiar with the Association's Education Standards for art therapy programs and the Education Program Approval Board (EPAB) Approval process (like "Accreditation"). From this process, it may look like either the EPAB or AATA are endorsing dual-degree programs, or worse, programs that are not art therapy in nature. If one were to look at the titles of master's degree programs gaining "Approval," I can see how those not familiar with the Association's and art therapy educational programs' commitment to art therapy training, art therapy identity, and the art therapy profession may think–and start rumors–that art therapy is becoming a counseling profession. Some may even believe that this tends to place art therapy in a decidedly secondary position with unfortunate and perhaps unintended consequences for graduates and the profession. That is not the case. Art therapy identity is preserved even in dual-degree programs.

The AATA has taken a leadership stance toward art therapy identity. One such stance was the creation of a position statement in favor and support of the art therapy license. The Association, in cooperation with sponsoring art therapy state associations, seeks licensure in states where that may be possible. The goal is to position the art therapy license as equivalent to other mental health licenses. Another stance toward a strong art therapy identity is illustrated by the sequence of meetings between the Association and federal and private insurance providers to include art therapy as one of the services covered. These are small steps in the desired path to affirm art therapy as an equal partner/profession within the health care and mental health arena.

Historically, the AATA has encountered times of turmoil and internal strife. Art psychotherapy versus art as therapy advocates created a polarization in the profession that persists today. There is also a difference in opinion among state art therapy associations that wish to seek art therapy license versus those that wish for alternative mental health licenses among practitioners who are exclusively art therapists versus those who ascribe to dual identity, or among art therapy educators who struggle with the decision of offering traditional art therapy programs versus art therapy as a specialization, coupled with the demands of state mental health legislation that govern the employability of art therapists. Personally and as president of the Association, I do not ascribe to conflict or a divided membership but to a membership body that is unified because of the richness that many individuals bring to the art therapy profession. The days to shine by stepping on one another are over; we shine brighter when working together. Art therapy is alive and well and will continue to thrive because of the human capital invested in this profession. I recognize that things have been difficult at times, but as an Association, we must let go and move forward. I am positive that we are moving to better times where conflict is left in the past where it belongs, and art therapists embrace diversity in training, practice, and credentialing while maintaining a strong art therapy identity.

I am proud to be an art therapist and a member and volunteer of the American Art Therapy Association.

References

American Counseling Association. (2005). *Code of ethics.* Retrieved February 25, 2013, from www.counseling.org

American Art Therapy Association. (2011). *Ethical principles for art therapists.* Retrieved February 25, 2013, from www.arttherapy.org on

ART THERAPIST IDENTITY CONFUSION DISORDER[1]

Cathy Malchiodi, PhD, LPCC, LPAT

Last year I posted a six-part series called "So You Want to Be an Art Therapist," covering education, credentials, and challenges involved in understanding art therapy as a profession. Just when I thought that I had pretty much described what you'll encounter in studying art therapy and practicing as an art therapist, the field may be undergoing its own form of "identity confusion."

In a previous post, I cited the lack of a specific listing for "art therapist" as a distinct profession in O*NET,[2] one of the most widely used and detailed job descriptors for job seekers, employers, and human resources (HR) staff in the United States. The good news is someone is apparently reading my blog (although I have been harping on this issue since at least 2004). There now is a placeholder page for "art therapist" on the O*NET site and a description of the predicted tasks of an art therapist in the workforce. There is a survey underway to identify additional information on the profession. Good news, huh? Okay, now for the bad news, or at least the "confusing" news.

In "Art Therapy Education," I reported on the movement within art therapy education to integrate counseling coursework to meet license standards for professional and/or mental health counselors at the state level. This movement has even led to the development of degree titles such as "art therapy counseling." The intent is to enhance the ability of art therapists to be part of the array of master's-level mental health professionals who practice psychotherapy. But where is the profession called "art therapist" now being positioned within the O*NET system? Not within a code that defines psychotherapy or mental health professions. It has been placed in a category right next door to recreation therapy, a bachelor's-level activity-oriented profession (Code 29.1125.00

---

1. The following essays originally appeared in Cathy Malchiodi's *Psychology Today* blog, "The Healing Arts," under the title, "So You Want to Be an Art Therapist, Part Seven: Art Therapist Identity Confusion Disorder" and "Art Therapy and Counseling: True Love or Convenience." They have been edited and are used with permission. The first essay was originally published January 12, 2012, and the second March 19, 2013.
2. O*NET is an internet database supported by the U.S. Department of Labor/Employment and Training Administration. It is a free online database and is the primary source for all U.S. occupational information.

for Recreation Therapy; Code 29.1125.01 for Art Therapy). Similarly, art therapy professors in higher education are now listed as part of "health specialty teachers" under the broader category of recreation therapy in O*NET's education section.

Honestly, I cannot wrap my head around this positioning of art therapy in a zip code next to recreation therapy and can now only wonder whether art therapy is finally spinning out of control due to its own long-standing and unresolved identity crisis. Historically, art therapy is a field that emerged from psychiatry and psychology, on the one hand, and visual art, on the other. Like many art therapists, I was educated in a tradition that even requires one to enter personal psychotherapy for experience and as part of preparation to work with clients. I have had to pass several licensing examinations, receive hundreds of hours of supervision, complete more than 3,000 hours of post-grad work, and become Board-Certified and licensed as an art therapist. Current students are taking anywhere from 60 to 90 graduate-level units to complete master's degrees–an undertaking that often requires student loans and a lot of personal sacrifice.

To my knowledge, recreation therapists do not routinely have to leap through these multiple and often expensive hoops; after all, they clearly perform as activity therapists and leisure specialists. In all fairness, at least one of the creative arts therapies, music therapy, has tended to see itself as an allied health profession such as recreation therapy, physical therapy, or occupational therapy. It is positioned in the same O*NET code as recreation therapy, but again bachelor's-level music therapists do not function as psychotherapists; they provide valuable services grounded in behavioral, educational, rehabilitation, and healthcare practices.

So where does this leave art therapy? Where does it leave you if you are pursuing art therapy as a career? I have no simple answers. I hope that by writing about this challenge, perhaps some art therapists are called to address it. We worked too hard as a field to promote this powerful approach to health and wellness to give up now. This is not the vision held by the founders of this field who worked toward a profession grounded in the practice of psychotherapy, even when art making was embraced as the "cure," in and of itself.

Addendum on January 21, 2012: The proposed classification of art therapy within the O*NET system has been moved to the Code 21 category (community and social services, where counseling is located). Whether it will finally end up in that category remains to be seen. A survey of art therapists will be conducted to see whether skill sets, work settings, and other career aspects match this category.

Art Therapy and Counseling:
True Love or Convenience?

Most art therapy educators say that the alliance between art therapy and counseling is a proactive move to make possible more options for graduating art therapy students to apply their degree in the workforce. They also frequently offer that an association with counseling emerged because art therapists inevitably learn to use verbal approaches within the context of their work. Others preach that bringing counseling into art therapy actually strengthens the field and is securing a healthy future for the field. Well, yes and no.

There is no doubt that any additional opportunity for a credential [state license] can help in subsequent searches for employment; remember, "art therapist" is not a licensed professional title in most states in the United States. But the real reasons for the marriage between art therapy and counseling are not often discussed and have largely remained the proverbial elephant in the living room.

Becoming a life partner with counseling did not emerge only because art therapy graduate programs were terrifically concerned about students' abilities to get great jobs, post-graduation. In reality, a decade ago, many art therapy graduate programs were starting to drop in enrollments. Why? Because realistically there were just not that many purely art therapy jobs out there. Art therapy master's degree programs are also mostly located in more expensive private colleges and universities, not in lower cost state institutions. In order for these programs to stay flush with students and tuition and for art therapy educators to keep their jobs, they needed to keep these degrees in operation. A marriage of convenience, so to speak, began to take place to grow the art therapy education industry.

It was also quite handy that counseling happened to be the only partner who would accept art therapy as a "related field" in terms of degree titles eligible for state licensure. In the late 1990s and the early 21st century, counseling needed practitioners to add to its own numbers to complete its own quest for licensure in all 50 states. Thus, a marriage of two professions began so that both parties could obtain desired status and security in a competitive mental health marketplace. Once this marriage gained momentum, art therapy/counseling graduate degrees started to emerge at a pace of several a year, some receiving more applicants than they can enroll, and others admitting far more students than can ever find specifically art therapy positions at a living wage. Art therapy education has become big business for many private institutions of higher learning as numbers of eager applicants seem pretty much endless, despite the lack of art therapy jobs afterward.

Like human marriages of convenience, the one art therapy has entered into is proving to present significant costs to the field. Just as in a marriage where one partner has more power, wealth, or family members than the other, that partner often has the upper hand in how the partnership plays out, consciously or not. Professional and mental health counseling have upward of 100,000 practitioners in the United States; art therapy possibly has 5,000 or 6,000, and many of those function under job titles other than "art therapist."[3] A growing number of master's degree art therapy programs are giving up "Master's in Art Therapy" on the diploma to take the name "Master's in Counseling" in order to benefit from what the partner's larger professional family has to offer in terms of privilege and opportunity. As more and more state counseling boards now turn to requiring the Council for Accreditation of Counseling and Related Educational Programs (CACREP) standards for eligibility for a counseling license, programs will be required to become counseling master's degrees by name. Eventually, according to CACREP standards, they will be required to hire new professors who hold doctorates in counselor education. To those individuals considering art therapy doctoral programs, understand that you may soon be ineligible to become professor in many art therapy graduate programs that adopt CACREP standards or are considering counseling accreditation. Perhaps art therapy could learn more about partnering from its creative arts therapy cousin music therapy that has faired well without a marriage to another profession.

---

3. Author's note: In a recent survey of art therapy programs in the United States, undertaken for this book, at least 90% of degree titles were not solely art therapy. They tended to be "Counseling With a Specialization in Art Therapy" or, at best, "Art Therapy and Counseling." A few years ago, the oldest graduate art therapy program in the country changed its degree title to "Art Therapy and Counseling."

Music therapy has focused on clarifying its unique identity, developing alliances within allied health and medicine, and demonstrating its value and position in the continuum of healthcare services. By some definitions, art therapy as a field is in its mid-40s age-wise in the United States, only a little bit younger than the field of music therapy. In the human lifecycle, one would expect that art therapy would be capable of living on its own by now and enjoying the accomplishments that come with independence, self-satisfaction, generativity, and equal partnerships. Instead, the field of art therapy seems to be finding itself increasingly stuck in a relationship that is taking time away from its own individuation as a profession. But what I find most disheartening is that rather than cultivating and expanding the profession, art therapy education has managed to get itself stuck in what may be turning into a bad romance. It certainly is one that entails increasing capitulation to a more powerful partner who is calling the regulatory shots and rules for licensure and license portability across state lines. More importantly, this dominant partner may eventually define standards of art therapy education and accreditation, relegating art therapy to the status of a technique within counseling rather than the dynamic, art-based, and creativity-driven profession that its founders and visionaries intended.

A STUDENT'S PERSPECTIVE

Brenda Maltz, BA, RN, CCM

Note: Brenda Maltz is a student in a dual-degree art therapy/mental health counselig graduate program at Antioch University-Seattle.

I heard that a few years ago, the American Counseling Association) and the AATA exchanged dialogue about aligning art therapy with the counseling profession. My assumption as a student in a dual-degree art therapy/counseling graduate program was that my future practice would be a marriage of the two disciplines. With the pressure to be licensed as a mental health counselor from a CACREP[1]-accredited school, I naturally assumed that I would accept the identity of licensed counselor but use my skills and training as an art therapist as a first line of intervention with clients. While I would like to consider myself solely an art therapist, the message I get is that this combination of license, credential and art therapy as a specialty focus, will allow gainful employment following graduation. I would like to be known as an "art psychotherapist" once I begin practice. It was interesting to me that the ACA has only recently come to consensus for defining their role and identity in the mental health field. I see the advantages of their organization to take a stand as a united front because they can make a difference for the profession and become political place holders for their future. But I am confused about the goals and intentions of the art therapy profession, and I wonder what can be learned from the ACA.

I suppose there are many opinions about this, as I expect there is an interest to see the art therapy profession stand on its own laurels. Is this possible? Take, for example, the case management profession.[2] Case management is not licensed; rather, a case manager can achieve "Certification" following an examination meeting the standards of the organizational board. Case managers have a variety of training backgrounds and licenses, most often in social work or nursing. One problem has been with reimbursement for services; however, as a united front with solid standards and good public relations, this field has grown expo-

1. CACREP is the accrediting body of the American Counseling Association.
2. "CCM" is "Certified Case Manager." Maltz has earned this certification.

nentially and is an integral part of the future of health care. As a case manager myself, I believe art therapy can learn from this model.

I think the art therapy profession should embrace the fact that, although other professionals and non-professionals may use art therapy techniques, there is so much more the art therapist is trained to understand. A physician can instruct someone how to take a blood pressure, but once the blood pressure is found to be abnormal, the doctor must use greater depth of knowledge to further assess and treat the individual. For this reason, I do not feel my professional identity would be threatened by sharing art therapy with others, particularly within a treatment team. In fact, in my opinion, that is where credibility from other professionals would define an art therapist's identity; the educated and trained art therapist who understands art process and content can contribute her or his expertise to the patient's treatment plan.

Sometimes, however, mental health practitioners are confused about the limits of patient artwork to reveal patient pathology. (Of course, I am speaking with the limited base of knowledge of a student.) I was fortunate to have a practicum experience in an in-patient psychiatric unit. I recall a particular incident working with a psychiatrist who appreciates how artwork can be a great source of diagnostic information. He asked me to pay attention to the artwork of a certain patient that day. I had asked a group of eight patients in a group to do the Silver "Draw a Story" assessment (Silver, 2001). The psychiatrist asked me to interpret a certain patient's image. I observed that the art of this particular patient was a little chaotic but not appreciably. The psychiatrist seemed a bit disappointed, as I think he was looking to confirm his suspicion that the patient was delusional. As a student, of course I questioned my observations, but I stayed with my training. I simply could not assume interpretation of something that was not revealed.

I have learned that miracles are not guaranteed to happen just because art materials are brought into therapy. Practicum only allowed me to parachute into the in-patient unit twice weekly for two quarters. I was pleasantly surprised just how much enthusiasm was present when I was there. I embraced the art therapy experience in the here and now moment, especially because that was all the time I was afforded. Even as a student, I could see the power of art and the image to make important connections for people.

I think increased involvement in the AATA could be a great benefit to students and AATA. I would like to see opportunities for senior
and junior art therapists to work together, perhaps in short on-site
practicums or student-oriented workshops, speaking tours, and greatly reduced or free admission to the annual conference. Together, experienced and up-and-coming art therapists could come together to
bring a vision into focus that might better define art therapy among
the art therapy community and for the general public as well. Stronger
advocacy for the profession is essential.

It seems to me that the art therapy profession needs to embrace diversity in order to grow. (While there is much lip service given to this kind
of approach, there is little actual action.) I would like to see increased
effort to encourage more multiculturalism and inclusion. It appears that
art therapy may be limited to a privileged few. There is so much art therapy can offer, especially when theories techniques and practices are enhanced by people of many cultures. The profession will grow stronger
once other ethnicities and cultures are better represented.

It also seems to me that the identity of the art therapy field would
strengthen with greater support for research. It would be helpful to
have access to formal research but also case studies and anecdotal stories of what works best from practical experience. The AATA journal
has been beneficial for me as a student.

I am curious about the work being done by creative disciplines outside art therapy; for example, those working with music, play, and
drama therapy. (Along with art therapy, our school has a drama therapy program.) Maybe it would be a good idea to reach out and collaborate with other approaches. It seems to me that there is much to
learn and share. I can envision an all-inclusive expressive therapy sum-
mit one day.

As a student, I would appreciate one strong statement from our profession that clearly defines what art therapy is. I have noticed that
members of our program faculty seem to have different views of how
they define themselves in reference to art therapy. Some identify themselves as counselors or therapists who use art as a modality in treating
clients. Others staunchly identify themselves as art therapists. The
message is confusing to me. I have come to realize that I will have to
decide as I further define myself as a practitioner during internship
and beyond. For now, I am sticking with art psychotherapy.

References

Silver, R. (2001). *Art as language: Access to thoughts and feelings through stimulus drawings.* Philadelphia: Psychology Press.

THE BEST THING EVER

Kim Newall, BFA

Note: Kim Newall is a master's student in a dual-degree art therapy/counseling educational program at Antioch University-Seattle.

Art therapy identity has been tracking me down for decades. I danced with the idea of it in the early stages of my visual arts career but turned instead to the path of professional artist and arts educator. All the while, I was most drawn to the psychological potential of process and image to express and transform a person from the core. This was my own experience as I created paintings and sculpture, which resurrected my lost memories and proved to me the shocking ability of the unconscious to reveal in photographic detail unmetabolized events calling for resolution. Once I had this experience, my primary interest in art focused on the collaboration between psyche and image. Although I tried to limit my efforts to studio practice and professional development, the intrapsychic exchange facilitated through color, line, texture, and form claimed my attention completely, and I entered a graduate program offering a dual degree in mental health counseling and art therapy.

Art therapy in a counseling context grounds me in a psychotherapeutic skill set and offers the practical advantages of licensure and connection to the more established counseling community. Art therapy expands my efficacy as a clinician by the profound power of the externalized image and through the advantage of making psychological processes visible. The language of image circumvents verbal defense, giving the psyche a fighting chance to slip past the ego, and for this reason art therapy is immensely powerful and requires training and expertise. I have learned this in my program and in my life, and this conviction is about to be field-tested as I will soon complete my coursework and begin internship in a rural community mental health agency.

The field of art therapy is young and still finding its place and its voice in the world and in me; we are developing together. This makes my developing identity feel tenuous and subject to a tendency toward premature solidification. Perhaps I am a microcosm of art therapy's developmental stage as well? I look for solid ground from which to practice and advocate. One outstanding aspect of my graduate training that provides a reassuring foundation includes the Expressive Therapies Continuum theoretical framework that gives a developmental model of image creation, material use, and information processing, as applied to the individuals I have worked with this far in my program (Hinz, 2009). In addition, the modeling provided by the essential mentorship and supervision I have received by experienced art therapists is a critical component of my education.

As I look to the next phase of my training as an intern, I am aware my identity as a counselor is more developed than my art therapist identity. Basic counseling skills have allayed my anxiety as a beginning clinician, and the context for counselors is more established and comprehensible. My budding art therapist self is both a novice and a pioneer, called to learn the skills while also challenging ignorance of and misconceptions about art therapy that place us in a "crafty" art class context.

As an art educator for 20 years, I know the value of an art class. However, the intersection of image, process, and psyche for the express purpose of creating change is too important to lose sight of. One of the strengths of art therapy is its ability to operate within any theoretical orientation and flow into the varied spaces of psychological exchange, whether office, studio, or client's home, as the change agent of transformation. I look forward to the experiences that will finally combine counselor and art therapist into a single entity, convincing me that art therapy is the "best thing ever" (Junge, 2013, personal communication.)

Reference

Hinz, L. (2009). *Expressive therapies continuum: A framework for using art in therapy.* New York: Routledge.

DEFINING VALUES: MANY SETTINGS, SINGULAR IDENTITY

Jordan S. Potash, PhD, ATR-BC, REAT, LCAT (NY)

My earliest days of being a student in art therapy involved heated discussion of what it meant to be an art therapist. We debated art therapy and art psychotherapy approaches. We listened to speakers describing the merits of professional registration within art therapy and receiving credentials in another professional discipline. We read the works of psychotherapists and artists alongside those of art therapists. Sometimes our learning came across as a great mosaic composed of artifacts from distant and disparate places. Other times it seemed like a clash of pattern and color. Still other times, it felt a bit like a scrapbook of collected theories held together by no more than hope and glue. For me, somehow it all coalesced into what it meant to be an art therapist.

Unlike some of my peers who entered the field to work in mental health, special education, or hospitals, I was interested in *community development.* I was specifically drawn to the way in which art therapy could enhance cross-cultural dialogues and foster social change. I saw, and continue to see, art as a unique way to build relationships and increase awareness of the wider world beyond our individual selves. Coming from a social action background, I was rooted in values of respect for others, acceptance of diverse perspectives, commitment to non-violent conflict resolution, being in service to the disenfranchised and empowerment of the marginalized. I carried these beliefs with me as I worked in therapeutic art education classrooms, public high school mental health programs, community mental health centers, community arts studios, private practices, and galleries under titles such as art therapist, mental health therapist, expressive arts programmer, and "art guy." My work is not limited to client encounters but extends to experiential learning, supervision, professional development, and community engagement. Yet despite the diverse ways in which I had to work in each setting, I held my social action values close and maintained that I was an art therapist and what I did was art therapy. I was always able to articulate the values of the social activist side of me, but how these aligned with the art therapist side of me was not always clear. Given the differences in where and how I worked, I tried to maintain an overall singular professional identity.

Preparing for this essay, I was curious as to what others meant by "professional identity." Merriam-Webster (2012) defined *identity* as "sameness of essential or generic character in different instances" and "the distinguishing character or personality of an individual." "Professional identity" specifically relates to "finding a professional home" and "common values and interests" with others in the same field (Granello & Young, 2012) Art therapists are not alone in the struggle for a definition that is constant across various settings. Gale and Austin (2003) cited that a collective professional identity as a counselor is threatened by differences in training, specializations, and affiliation with specific associations. In providing recommendations to combat this threat, the authors attempted to distill common beliefs that unify the profession. While attending the 2010 Joint World Conference on Social Work and Social Development in Hong Kong, I heard social workers lament how social work has lost its identity and needs to return to its beliefs or what were often referred to as *core values*. Attempting to explicate values as it pertains to identity was Packard's (2009) focus for counseling psychologists' professional identity, as well as Rogers's (1951) principles for client-centered therapists. Given the centrality of values in defining identity, I am left asking myself about the values that I see as maintaining myself as an art therapist.

Challenges to Identifying Art Therapy Identity

I was unable to find a list of art therapy values, but a look at the definition of the profession offered by various art therapy organizations helped guide my thinking. The American Art Therapy Association (2012) describes "professional relationship" by "creating art and reflecting on the art products and processes, people can increase awareness of self and others." The British Association of Art Therapists (2011) refers to "relationship" and the "three-way process." The Canadian Art Therapy Association (2012) speaks of "facilitating self-exploration and understanding" while the Australian-New Zealand Art Therapy Association (2012) mentions, "emphasis is on the process of creating and meaning-making." Each of these definitions points to different facets of art therapy and informs a set of beliefs, but Wadeson (2002) [an American] implied that a unifying art therapy value is simply "our enormous creativity" (p. 83). In terms such as relationship, awareness, understanding, meaning-making, and creativity, I see connections and parallels to my social action allegiance.

Attempting to consolidate a core set of values for art therapists is a challenge. Perhaps the greatest difficulty is that claiming identity implies boundaries. I feel that in our desire to be accepted by others, art therapists have been quick to say that we can do everything that others can do, only better because we have either art or psychological training. In our attempts to prove our adaptability, I am afraid that we have at times lost sight of our core; that is, a foundation that unites art therapists across various work settings and job titles. It is not enough to say that our uniqueness stems from a belief in the power of art. Art is not unique to us; it is shared by therapists who make use of art and artists who offer their skills to others. At the same time, it is not our psychological training either, as that is shared by other health care professionals and sensitively attuned artists.

It sometimes helps me to think about art therapy professional identity development along Sue and Sue's (1999) racial/cultural identity development model. Like many other similar models, this one begins with a lack of awareness of difference between oneself and the dominant group. Then in realizing one's difference, the individual may identify with the dominant at the expense of losing one's own culture, confront the dominant to show difference, value one's own culture while devaluing the dominant, and finally lives one's culture in mutual respect alongside others. I can see where art therapists have been at all these stages, whether we see psychology or art as the dominant group in which we need to fit. When we are disregarded by therapists for not being disciplined or educated enough and shunned by artists for dismissing or misusing art, we find ourselves wondering who we are and how to demonstrate it. The key to arriving at the final stage of Sue and Sue's model is to be secure enough in oneself to withstand challenges and to know how our differences give us something to contribute to the greater community. We do not need to accept dominant ideas; rather, *we need to be ourselves, which means knowing what we believe and adopting a stance.* Even as I write this last sentence, I can see how the social action side of me informs my professional identity.

What can make it difficult to define our identity is art therapists' tendency to go with trends in mental health and wellness. When the field began, we aligned with Freudian ideas of psychodynamics, the dominant idea of the time. Although we might have chosen Jungian psychology, given the use of spontaneous and deliberate image production or Humanistic psychology with the emphasis on creativity and health, at that particular historical period, Freud was more accepted, and the two major theorists in art therapy were psychodynamically oriented. We see this pattern of adapting to the dominant belief system continue today. As an example, when I was a student, we were told that the value of art therapy was in the fact that art bypasses the censor of the "superego"–a Freudian term–bringing unconscious material into awareness. Now many describe the value of art therapy as bypassing the "cognitive brain" to access the emotional brain.

Embedded in this change is not only the description and language of how we explain one of the benefits of art therapy. Beneath the surface is an enduring belief in how art making brings unknown experiences into awareness. While the neuroscience explanation may help us stay current, the lack of clearly articulating the underlying value can confuse what we actually believe. Do we believe that art leads to the unconscious or to the limbic system? Or do we simply mean that art yields authentic, profound, primitive, instinctual communication that is necessary for self-knowledge and healing? I am comfortable with multiple explanations as to how art works, but I think it is important that we firmly state our beliefs of what art therapy offers.

Values that Inform My Art Therapy Professional Identity

As stated, identity relates to a consistency across diverse situations and adherence to particular ideas. I want to emphasize ideas over techniques or practices. The former are more enduring and inform a philosophy and belief system of working whereas the latter emphasize activity that can be easily disconnected from the reason for doing certain tasks. There is no lack of books on art therapy techniques, but these are just things to do with clients and do little to stipulate a core concept unique to art therapy. As I look back over the positions in which I have served, the following are what I identified as the art therapy values and principles that allowed me and continue to allow me to maintain my professional identity across a range of settings. In their own ways, each is intimately tied to social action values, such as diversity acceptance, relationship equality and democratic engagement:

Art

The crux of art therapy is the creation and presence of art. I agree with B. Moon's (2009) broad use of art as related to the term *image* to refer to both internal and externally produced ones, as well as the meanings and associations connected to them. Art is a platform for expression that is a valid form of understanding self, other, and world in its own right. Although it may at times require written or verbal language to further enhance, elucidate, or illuminate its meaning, without a relatively consistent place for art, there is no art therapy.

Authenticity

Working with an art therapist entails a professional relationship in which the primary goal is the client's creation of art that strives to increase her or his knowledge and awareness about him or her self, relationships, and world. While relationship is the cornerstone of all the helping service professions, it is not necessarily the case in fine arts or art education. In those circumstances, art can be a means to an end—whether as communication or as commodity—but is not always a co-partner in change. Within the art studio, I strive to establish an authentic relationship with my clients so they immerse in creating and interpreting art in order to yield insights that can result in being a better and healthier individual, partner, relative, friend, colleague, and citizen. Through increases in awareness, clients can transpose what they have learned in the studio for personal, interpersonal, and societal changes.

Emotions

With emotions as the starting place, art therapists allow for expression, communication, reflection/contemplation, and containment, sometimes simultaneously and sometimes independently. Within my practice of art therapy, emotions drive art making by keeping art focused on personal experience. Just as psychotherapy is not taken up by generic or social conversations about politics and the weather or any other topic that can be discussed with a friend or stranger on the bus, art therapy is not a matter of still lifes or decorative arts. (That is not to say that there is not a place for these things or that all art is not about emotional expression.) Sometimes the best direction for art therapy is not expression but containment or contemplation and reflection on one's inner state (Franklin, 2000). Other times it may be best to focus on the world (Wix, 2009) and on one's own reactions to societal ills and solutions (Potash, 2011). Using my therapeutic judgment, I try to help clients decide how they want to engage or disengage from emotions.

Aesthetics

Both the art product and the creative process are active ingredients in art therapy. Through the creative process, as clients engage materials and images, change occurs. However, all too often, I hear that in art therapy the creative process is more important than the art product. This idea may help create a nonjudgmental stance (judgment is something art therapists have tried to distance themselves from—a fine arts and art education inheritance), but this lack of focus on or judgment about the art in art therapy can diminish the value of the created art product. I have found it useful to help focus clients toward creating art that is well formed and visually and aesthetically articulate in order to better convey a client's personal narrative. I do not impose my own aesthetics, but I ask them to reflect on the range of colors, lines, and details to ensure that the resulting piece feels complete, whole, and personally meaningful. In this way, the art has a better chance of embodying emotion (Schaverien, 1992) and serving as a conduit for expression (Kramer, 1966). Holding on to this idea pushes me and my clients to deeper and more genuine levels of expression that are inaccessible to stereotypical, thoughtless, impoverished, or superficial images, on the one hand, or over-worked, highly crafted, or academically governed rules of art on the other.

Mutuality

Clients, art therapists, and art co-collaborate to arrive at mutual and shared understanding. The idea of being a clever sage who can look deeply into an image and arrive at its true message is certainly appealing to some art therapists. It recalls the status of oracles and tealeaf readers, but it fosters a dependence on the professional interpreter that can be a hindrance to emotional health. The concept of the three-way relationship (Schaverien, 1992) underscores the respect and commitment I have for images, the creative process, and the strong belief that clients can actively discover their own meanings. Believing in the three-way process holds me to democratic values by maintaining my attention to the relationship that is established among art therapist, client, and art product and process (B. Moon, 2009). To keep me grounded in this value, I am guided by C. Moon's (2002) ideas on relational aesthetics, which shifts my thinking from judgment, critique, and assessment to empathy, acceptance, and meaning-making.

Imagination

Art therapists see art making as a channel to promote imagination and creativity, which leads to greater perspectives and emotional flexibility. Imagination is a core idea of art therapy that informs every aspect of the image (Maclagan, 2005). Imagination prompts an image to come into being by allowing us a certain amount of freedom to represent what is not physically present or only exists as an internal experience. At the same time, imagination encourages both clients and art therapists to come up with meanings and interpretations for the art that is created. In this sense, art is not locked into a single meaning but given the flexibility of multiple meanings informed by metaphor, archetype, culture, and life experience (McNiff, 1992). Fostering imagination is one step on the path to greater creativity and flexibility.

Holism

Art therapists embrace a holistic perspective that includes a range of artistic styles and forms, each with its own validity and necessity. While respecting some of art therapy's roots in projective drawing, art making in art therapy leads to more than diagnosis. Instead it can offer a holistic view of clients, including their developmental level, defenses, cultural expectations, problem-solving skills, and comfort with art making. I have found two theories to be particularly helpful in guiding me: The Expressive Therapies Continuum highlights a place for all forms of art making and provides a framework for how to understand the clients' relationship to the creative process, as well as how to best work with them (Hinz, 2009; Kagin & Lusebrink,

1978). Understanding that a client is using art for kinesthetic release, emotional containment, or symbolic understanding is highly valuable in accepting clients' current circumstances and helps me facilitate the course of art therapy. The Great Round of the Archetypal Stages of the Mandala (Kellogg, 1984) provides a way to broaden my view of images beyond personal narrative in order to see how client concerns relate to the general and existential human condition. Although the ideas are Jungian ones, Kellogg's arrangement of 13 image patterns demonstrates the holistic value of all experiences and images rather than label some according to psychiatric classifications of dysfunction.

Closing Reflection

I recognize that any one of these values and principles taken in isolation can pertain to many fields, but together they form the core of what being an art therapist means to me. We are a relatively new profession with a complicated ancestry. It takes many steps to reach the end stages of an integrated identity. Because I maintain these same values and principles in all settings, I do not find a conflict as to whether I am situated in a studio, sitting in an office, or standing on the street offering what looks like psychotherapy, art education, or community work. I may work differently when with an individual struggling with anxiety than I do with a group of people struggling to challenge discrimination, but my values and philosophy remain the same. The essence of what I am doing remains the same because what I am doing is art therapy, and what I am is an art therapist.

References

American Art Therapy Association (2012). *Art therapy: Definition of the profession.* Available at http://www.americanarttherapyassociation.org/aata-aboutus.html

Australia-New Zealand Art Therapy Association. (2012). *About arts therapy.* Available at http://www.anzata.org/about-arts-therapy/

British Association of Art Therapists. (2011). *What is art therapy?* Available at http://www.baat.org/art_therapy.html

Canadian Art Therapy Association. (2012). *What is art therapy?* Available at http://catainfo.ca/cata/study-at/

Franklin, M. (2000).The yoga of art and the creative process: Listening to the devine. In M. Farrelly-Hansen (Ed.), *Spirituality and art therapy: Living the connection.* London & Philadelphia: Jessica Kingsley.

Gale, A., & Austin, B. (2003). Professionalism's challenges to professional counselors' collective identity. *Journal of Counseling and Development, 81*(1), 3–10.

Granello, D., & Young, M. (2012). *Counseling today: Foundations of professional identity.* Upper Saddle River, NY: Pearson.

Hinz, L. (2009). *Expressive therapies continuum: A framework for using art in therapy.* London: Routledge.

Kagin, S., & Lusebrink, V. (1978). The expressive therapies continuum. *The Arts in Psychotherapy, 5,* 171–180.

Kellogg, J. (1984). *Mandala: Path of beauty.* Williamsburg, VA: Mandala Assessment and Research Institute.

Kramer, E. (1966). The problem of quality in art. In E. Ulman & P. Dachinger (Eds.), *Art therapy in theory and practice.* Chicago: Magnolia Street.

Maclagan, D. (2005). Re-imagining art therapy. *International Journal of Art Therapy, 10*(1), 23–30.

McNiff, S. (1992). *Art as medicine.* Boston, MA: Shambhala.

Merriam-Webster (2012). *Identity.* Available at http://www.merriam-webster.com/dictionary/identity

Moon, B. (2009). *Existential art therapy. The canvas mirror* (3rd ed.). Springfield, IL: Charles C Thomas.

Moon, C. (2002). *Studio art therapy: Cultivating the artist identity in the art therapist.* London & Philadelphia: Jessica Kingsley.

Packard, T. (2009). The 2008 Leona Tyler Award Address: Core values that distinguish counseling psychology: Personal and professional perspectives. *The Counseling Psychologist, 37*(4), 610–624.

Potash, J. (2011). Art therapists as intermediaries for social change. *Journal of Art for Life, 2*(1), 48–58.

Rogers, C. (1951). *Client-centered therapy: Its current practice, implications and theory.* London: Constable & Company.

Schaverien, J. (1992). *The revealing image: Analytical art psychotherapy in theory and practice.* London: Routledge.

Sue, D., & Sue, D.W. (1999). *Counseling the culturally different: Theory and practice.* (3rd ed.). New York: Wiley.

Wadeson, H. (2002). Confronting polarization in art therapy. *Art Therapy: Journal of the American Art Therapy Association, 19*(2), 77–84.

Wix, L. (2009). Aesthetic empathy in teaching art to children: The work of Friedl Dicker-Brandeis in Terezin. *Art Therapy: Journal of the American Art Therapy Association, 26*(4), 152–158.

AN EVOLVING IDENTITY:
A MIRROR OF ONE'S PERSONAL HISTORY

Arthur Robbins, EdD, HLM

Practitioners often confront their own particular life stories vis-à-vis the patients they work with or a particular theoretical bias that guides them in the therapeutic dialogue. Consequently, I believe an appropriate way of opening up the topic of art therapy identification can be one of sharing with you, the reader, my own personal narrative. This story contains landmarks of personal memories that place me at the crossroads of professional expression and commitment. I've worn many hats along the way: psychologist, psychoanalyst, art therapy pioneer, teacher, supervisor, and administrator interfaced with the life challenges of being husband, father, and grandfather. These overlapping roles contributed to a rather complex conception of what art therapy work was all about. This, in turn, impacted an evolving art therapy identity. Many of these currents easily could have be applied to my other professional duties as well. At each juncture point of this story, I will pause and comment about its particular influence to the development of my professional self.

I remember my family as neat, orderly, and clean. Furniture was covered with plastic protection. An amusing memory comes to mind: My mother would vacuum the rug as the guests left the dinner table. The first time this occurred in front of my wife-to-be, she found it hard to believe. Yet, despite it all, the family was greatly involved with the topic of aesthetics. Both my sister and mother would talk endlessly about home decorating, and later on my sister became one of the outstanding interior decorators of Montreal. Interspersed in this dialogue was my father, a manufacturer of artificial flowers. He would present his newest creation for comments and reflections. I, in contrast, was banished to the sandbox in the backyard. This was at least better than my first two years of life, when I was often swaddled in a baby carriage exposed to the sun, cutting off any mobility to explore the world. I carried the family's hidden sloppy, dirty self and became very ashamed. I could do nothing right but invariably found myself in trouble. I was fascinated with fire and played with the flames of the stove unless my blind grandmother smelled that something was wrong and cried out

for help, "He's at the stove again!" This preoccupation of mine extended to fire engines, where I would surreptitiously pull fire alarms if I
was not watched with a sharp eye.

As a growing professional, I soon learned that disorder and mess
could lead to a new creation of something original. Being an isolate, I
also went my own way in terms of my thinking and professional contributions. This may have contributed to being an odd-ball, but it did
permit me to put together fresh and innovative ideas into a new aesthetic gestalt. The fire inside me contributed to the passion in my work
and an ability to destroy things so that I could build something from
its ashes.

My early conception about art had something to do with making
things pretty and beautiful, something I knew I couldn't and didn't
want to do. In fact, I remember my nightmares about taking art classes. Only later on in sculpting classes did I learn that beauty had something to do with transformation–changing the inanimate into the ani-
mate, which invited the viewer to travel past one's personal limitations
of reality.

More information about my background: My mother was an or-
phan who was shipped from one uncle to another. Her world was dangerous and held little security. Her father abandoned her and her
mother early in life, for a number of love affairs and flirtations. Obviously, from my mother's perspective, men could not be trusted, and
I was kept under her watchful eye so that I would not "grow into one
of "those." Her mother died while she was young, and she developed
an intense connection to her blind grandmother. My father also lost
his mother at an early age and never quite fit into his new family with
his stepmother. He became an outsider who joined with my mother,
expounding the same attitudes of never fitting into any community.

My backyard became the playground for creations. I would dig dark
tunnels and fortresses and build a community that became a reflection
of my own imagination. Here, the roots of creativity and expression
were born and became a form of my survival (Robbins, 2006).

The entire family held little hope for my future. I could do nothing
right. Later on, I called on this internal aggression to help me become
an extemporaneous teacher and a provocative therapist and supervisor. A turning point took place at age 13 at my Bar Mitzvah. Sitting in
the audience was my mother. I can still envision her with her hand

held over her face. I intuitively knew what she was thinking: "My son will bring shame upon all of us." Observing that depressed inward face, I experienced a surge of rage and refused to comply with the projection. I gave, in fact, one of the best speeches in my life. They were all surprised. Sadly, however, this seemed to be just an incidental occurrence. Yet I do feel that this became a piece of experience that reorganized my identity. Today, I give speeches without notes and trust that my unconscious will organize what comes out of my mouth.

As a young adult, I was drawn to women who reminded me of my mother. They seemed to be nice, looked pretty, and were familiar. Fortunately, the toxic image of my mother was so clear in my consciousness that I knew better then to marry someone like her. They often say that summer camp romances don't last. However, in my own particular experience, my wife-to-be and I met as co-counselors, and the experience was an eye opener. Instead of trying to please the woman and never succeeding, I felt appreciated and seen. She was sensuous and physical and opened up a whole new world of communication for me. Sensuousness then became an early part of my contacting and reaching patients. The sensory form of being that initiates contact now has been substantiated through brain research. I now know the importance of body-to-body communication that is facilitated by a sensuous way of knowing one another. I often ask my students to walk and talk like their patients or become the image that their art creates. Just to clarify things, when I use the word "sensuous," I am referring to the senses not to libidinal communication, not that that is not important also.

Let me return to my personal story. I needed to find out about myself, and psychology became my obvious choice. Yet my grades were mediocre. But all this miraculously changed when I met my wife. As our relationship developed, something remarkable occurred. Everything now flowed and seemed to organize itself into high-level conceptions. At the time we were courting, the Korean War was on, and I was given a three-month deferment that ended at the end of the academic year. I had but three months from the start to finish my doctoral thesis. A doctorate could lead to a commission where, if married, we might then be able to live with one another in the army. I collected data that were part of a bigger research project and without notes started to dictate my thesis. Her smiling, approving face seemed to ignite my imagination. At times she refused to type what I dictated. She simply said, "You can do better." "It's my thesis," I complained. "I am part of this," she responded, "and I think you can do better." The thesis was completed in the allotted three-month time, and I passed my final presentation. The committee's parting words went as follows: "It may not be the finest thesis but it was the fastest in Teacher's College history." The thesis was a tight 54 pages.

I learned from this experience how another person's belief in one's self becomes pivotal in opening up a space between one's self and another. The development of an open space makes it possible to see and experience psychic phenomena on multiple levels. Being seen became a landmark principal of my psychological work. Mirroring, being it in verbal or non-verbal therapy, became an important part of working with people.

Back to the story: My degree became a ticket to obtaining a commission as a First Lieutenant in the Army Medical Service Corps. I held the unique distinction of being the only psychology officer present in the war zone of Korea. With a battery of technicians under me, I would administer Rorschach Ink Blots Test to soldiers who manifested symptoms of an emotional breakdown. My job was to offer information regarding a differential diagnosis. One year of training with the Rorschach was little for such a daunting task. However, after working with 2030 protocols a week, I developed an artistic sense and feel for the patient's response to these ink blots. Here, I learned how form, color, space, and texture interplayed with personality expression. Later on, this background became an important point of departure in my working with art therapy expression.

After the army, I was anxious to move on and obtain psychoanalytic training. I recall at my wedding I was introduced to my long-lost uncle. He came up to me and said, "Do you know who I am? I am your Uncle Jules." Little did I know that Uncle Jules was one of the founders of the first non-medical psychoanalytic institutes in America. I soon also discovered three close relatives who were psychoanalysts. All of them were half brothers and sisters of my father. They were family that was unknown to me while I was growing up. I instinctively knew that Jules Nydes was going to become an important part of my development. Jules became my teacher, supervisor, and mentor. He also, in my eyes, was a powerful male figure who supported his nephew.

Something inside of me became more balanced. There was a better flow between my masculine and feminine energies that became important in my work with patients. There became a rhythm between the inside and outside, and problems in flow became an important part of dealing with therapeutic expression. I also learned that energy emanated from a different source then the self. The self was part of a later development that embodied our internalizations, attitudes, and aspirations. For me, the soul is there at birth ready to be nurtured if the environment is safe and holding, so that there is little internal conflict between the soul and the self. It was part of an inner light and an ambiance that embodied the life spirit of a person. This soul could also be one of an artist that explored light and dark as well as transformation and life spirit. For me, the soul was a source of energy that was never held in my family. A transformed psychic self only started to develop when I was a young adult. Before this transformation, in its place, I saw myself as ugly, shameful, and full of reaction formations. I was the destructive rebel who would go nowhere in life. My self was contaminated with all kinds of projections that took me many years to separate from.

Upon graduating from a psychoanalytic institute, and while I was still in my analysis, I knew that something was still missing. The mystery of my unconscious was at work and I intuitively knew I wanted to sculpt. In the past, I both hated and feared art since artistically I could create nothing that was pretty and nice. I still recall attending my first sculpting class: I brought my wife along for protection. I peeked in, and the teacher caught me sticking my head through the door and proclaimed, "Vell, vat are you vaiting for?" She was an earthy Russian lady who, much to my surprise, took pleasure and delight in my clay creations. I started to develop a different notion of artistic expression. I travelled from clay to stone but was still on a search for the medium that touched me deeply.

I enrolled in a welding course offered at San Miguel De Allende, Mexico. Here I discovered how melted metal could dance before your eyes. The fire inside of me found an expression. My fondest memories are of traveling to a junk yard, searching for discarded pieces of metal, and welding them into new shapes and forms. Somewhere, I was also responding to the discarded pieces of my parents that were lodged inside of me and giving them new shape, form, and meaning.

When I started the course at San Miguel, the instructor recommended that I first draw the art piece I had in mind. "That's not my way!" I retorted. He responded in turn, "Then, I will have nothing to do with you." However, when I showed him my first completed piece, he became duly impressed and decided to share his own work with me. The outsider in me, who had to go his own way, was very much at work. I was, of course, idiosyncratic and different. Yet because I fit into no established order, I was free enough to not be restricted by too many rules and regulations.

In the mid-1960s, I "stumbled" on a part-time teaching position introducing art students to psychology at Pratt Institute[1] in New York. Coincidentally, this was the very place my sister always wanted to attend, but this door was closed to her because of a lack of funds. I was both dismayed and impressed by these young artists. They hated everything I had to offer. I soon learned not to impose my own ideas of psychology but to follow their particular flow. This made a lasting imprint on me. I gave up the restrictions of psychoanalytic language and let them be in charge of the flow of material. Since then I have never believed in syllabi or treatment plans. Experiences evolved out of personal interactions, and theory could be built out of this experience. Having a pre-arranged theory simply got in my way. Yet I held inside of me an inner core of discipline of research and clinical development that served as an internal anchor and permitted me to roam far afield.

In the meantime, I was requested by the summer community that I lived in to present a talk on creativity. It became a great success. This seemed to stimulate my imagination. Something quite remarkable evolved: Why couldn't I put together psychology, creativity, and art? Somewhere I was also working on the integration of the different parts of myself that were struggling for wholeness. I approached Joe Garai, the chairperson at Pratt, and asked, "How did he feel about starting an art therapy program?" I showed him my plans and outline, and he finally said, "We'll be partners." Joe didn't know too much about clinical work because his background was as an academic child psychologist. However, he was the insider who gave me permission to run with the ball. The time was ripe for something new and different to happen.

---

1. Pratt Institute, a school of art and design in New York City.

The year was 1970, and a good deal of change was about to occur. Four different art therapy training programs, located in different parts of the country, all announced the presence of a new and innovative program called *art therapy*. Pratt was one of those first four. None of us knew about the other three programs; each thought we had something special and unique to offer. In fact, this was true. Art therapy programs developed and grew in their separate ways. It was hard to believe that all four programs belonged to the same field. Today, I think, that to a certain extent this still holds true; each program has developed its separate identity called "art therapy." They are usually an expression of the faculty who started the program. New applicants for programs should discover the differences, particularly from graduates, and find the style of teaching that best suits them.

As for our own theoretical orientation at Pratt, I knew of two giants in the art therapy field: Margaret Naumburg and Edith Kramer. Neither, I felt, represented the breadth of what I believed the field could offer. I started to build a theory that came out of my own life experience as well as the field work of the students. I soon learned that some students were happy working in education, others in rehabilitation, while some went in a strong clinical direction. The soul of the artist bound all of them together. My job as an instructor was to offer a climate where they could find their own particular professional direction. At the same time, I introduced a point of view that was quite unique. Experience with patients started in the first semester of the program. As a result, they learned by doing, not just by lectures and reading. I also believed that work with transference and countertransference was unavoidable.

Many students had little or no personal therapy. They immediately became full of personal powerful introjections and projections that shook the bottom of their existence. They needed processing, and the faculty was there for them in supervisory groups to go from personal to the professional to the theoretical. However, I understood and respected the curriculum of those programs that kept field experience to the second year and barely touched transference and countertransference material. This was simply not our direction. Obviously, the type of training students were exposed to at Pratt arose out of my personal need for action and passion as well as feeling and touching the essence of therapeutic process. This equally applies to those students who desired placements with art as therapy as well as applicants who basically wanted a clinical experience.

In the beginning, art therapy program students were hard to come by. Four food services students wandered into our office. Before they knew it, they were enrolled in our program. They then proceeded to create a therapeutic catering unit with veterans. I excitedly shared this experience in an early meeting of the American Art Therapy Association. I still remember a former president responding, "My grandmother makes bagels, but that's not art therapy." So we became the "Bagel Therapists" of America. Because we were known for experimentation, we also developed a somewhat derisive reputation as a "touchy, feely" program. Yet the theory and grounding that the students were presented was of a sophisticated and complex order. Here, once again, I went out of my sandbox and put a new frame of what I thought art therapy could be.

With each year, something new was added. Movement could not be separated from the experience of an art image. For many, aesthetics could only become alive while moving into space and form. Slowly a creative arts approach evolved. While students brought a background in visual art, they were free to utilize other modalities and even develop the techniques to talk and process with their clients. Again, I wish to emphasize that, for me, an art therapist has the soul of an artist and a commitment to work with psychic experience. Psychic experience is one of exploring all levels of consciousness. This includes the spiritual, the bodily, the intra-psychic, as well as the inter-personal.

Unfortunately, the process of institutionalization increasingly defined standards as to what art therapy was about. I knew one of my basic books, Castaneda's *Tales of Power,* would never be accepted by an accreditation team. Consequently, I built an extensive acceptable syllabus and offered my own unique interpretation to the material.

The first years of art therapy were combative and competitive in the American Art Therapy Association. I still remember Edith Kramer addressing me: "Some people know to tend their rose garden while others think they can take care of the whole forest." I responded, looking straight at her, "Many confuse art education and art therapy." In retrospect, I am deeply embarrassed by this interchange. Inside of me there is an Edith Kramer, a Margaret Naumburg, as well as a resource of all my life experiences. My goal is to accept all of them and not to split or project one part on to the other. I strive for wholeness even though I have trouble getting there. Splitting is just a convenient way of getting rid of our hated parts.

In my youth, I held the belief that I could be Art Robbins wherever I lived. I now know better. All of us need a community that reflects and mirrors back our attitudes and beliefs. I am a New Yorker. I find the energy and cultural variety opens up my field of connection. I still remember buying a house in the suburbs and selling it in three months. It became my existential experience, and the suburban climate simply did not reflect who I, or my family, was. I also know that my house in the country seems to heal my soul. It is quiet and close to nature. Also having taught in Europe for 40 years, the encountering of different cultures and societies has offered me a sharp etching of the differences and similarities that are part of all of our being.

There is a new movement afoot called an "umbrella identity" so that a number of disciplines ban together to achieve certain legal gains by the sheer numbers of their organization. There is something both positive and negative about this development. On the one hand, large numbers facilitate the legalization of a profession. Many professionals see this as positive. On the other hand, I also witness students becoming part of other disciplines and losing their entire identification with their roots of the soul of an artist. Despite our umbrellas, we should offer support groups that have similar attitudes and values for the field of art therapy. This is especially true after we graduate the students from our particular programs.

In this complicated world, we make all kinds of compromises. Hopefully, we discover definitions of art therapy practice that preserve the essence of an artist and still allow ample room to grow in many directions. As to art therapy's future, we will continue to build a complex disciplined and multilevel theory that will provide the foundation for survival. This foundation offers us a core of knowledge that does not put up boundaries but opens up the field for expression.

From my personal background, you can easily ascertain a number of important cornerstones: The outsider image permits me to go my own way. I have a penetrating mother who lives inside of me who can function and help me be deep and insightful as a teacher and a therapist. The father inside of me knows how to hold and create an atmosphere of safety. I equally work with both the inside and the outside; I can be messy and destructive and still rebuild and create. Identity process is fluid and governed by our roots as well as the new experiences that occur over a lifetime. I believe that knowing our personal story gives us an opportunity to make choices at the inevitable crossroads that are associated with personal and professional identity. Being bound by our personal story only furthers rigidity and a squelching of creativity. However, accepting our story permits us to take the good parts of it to create bridges into the unknown.

At 84, I look forward to the mystery that the future holds for me. Dealing with the crisis of becoming an older professional stimulates many old and new conflicts. The enlargement of the story would take up an entire new chapter. What is most important to emphasize are the inevitable life crises and conflicts that offer us opportunities to enlarge our sense of self while we rediscover our roots with a new rhythm. The spiral of increasing complexity, separation, and loss, coupled with transforming experiences, become landmarks of a life-long professional and personal identity process. The story that has unfolded serves as a frame for my own personal subjectivity. All of us have a story to be told that gives us our own particular uniqueness to the notion of professional identity. Consequently, any superimposed definition must be as broad as possible, allowing each professional to grow into her or his own uniqueness. What we need is a respect for individual differences and a recognition that in our separateness we can also discover our shared commonalities. My hope in sharing these various cross currents with you is a holding environment will develop that allows all of us to feel part of something bigger—where personal artistry and life experiences can offer us meaning and belonging and still retain room for individuality, where we can have the pleasure of identifying ourselves as an Art Therapist.

Reference

Robbins, A. (2006). Moving in and out of the sandbox. In M. B. Junge & H. Wadeson (Eds.), *Architects of art therapy*. Springfield, IL: Charles C Thomas, Publisher, Ltd.

WEARING MY PROFESSIONAL IDENTITY ON MY SLEEVE

Marcia L. Rosal, PhD, ATR-BC, HLM

I am a daughter. I am a sister. Although I consider myself an American, I am also half Guatemalan and half Italian. I am a spouse. I am a friend and I have friends. I am a colleague. I am a neighbor. I am a book lover and a lover of movies; I love food and love to eat. I am also an art therapist.

I am an art therapist. Since entering an art therapy master's program nearly 40 years ago, I have never hesitated telling any interested party that I am an art therapist. I inhabit this mantel totally and without abandon. So happy am I to be an art therapist that it is a surprise when identity is brought up as a thorny issue. How could I have ever been anything else? I can't fathom doing anything else. I don't worry that others do not know what art therapy is. When I encounter people without this understanding, I am happy to offer them an explanation. Even after pursuing a doctoral degree in educational psychology, I never thought of myself as anything but an art therapist.

My undergraduate work was in art education. I chose this major because, for as long as I remember, I wanted to work with children and engage with them in art making; as an adolescent, I did not know about art therapy. My undergraduate education was in the tradition of Viktor Lowenfeld and his successors at Pennsylvania State University. Some of you will remember that Lowenfeld coined the term *art education therapy* in his writings (Lowenfeld, 1957). I loved the book, *Creative and Mental Growth,* which he published with Brittain in 1970. Although I was not one of the lucky few art education students in my class selected for that one special education school placement to do student teaching, my goal was to work with special needs children. My disappointment soon turned to good fortune because I had the chance to work with children with special needs soon after graduation. On Penn State's campus, there was an assessment classroom. Teachers from surrounding counties who were concerned about how to best address the needs of a particular child referred students to this program for assessment and educational rehabilitation. Although I had many roles in this classroom, the one I cherished most was creating art with the children.

One day after an art lesson, the lead teacher told me that she was impressed with what I was able to do with the kids that day. She asked several questions, most of which I readily answered. However, she also asked whether I could assess the meaning or evaluate the art created. I explained that I could only describe the skills the children used, whether these skills were age appropriate, and what they said about the art; I did not have training in using the art as a psychological assessment tool. Her inquiry inspired me to go the library, where I found three books on art therapy: Kramer (1971) and Naumburg (1966, 1973). After devouring these books, I was certain that art therapy was *my profession,* and off I went to art therapy graduate school.

While working toward an art therapy degree, my background in art education was useful. I received an internship placement in a school setting because of the art education degree. At one point in my career, I acquired a job working with children diagnosed with autism in a school system in Louisiana because of my art education teacher certification. Finally, that art education degree helped me secure a faculty position at Florida State University because the department wanted to launch an art therapy program in the Department of Art Education.

Even when considering these events, I never thought of myself as anything other than an art therapist. Yet I found that having art education in my background opened doors for me that might have been closed otherwise. This may be similar to what is happening with the profession today. Many art therapists find themselves needing counseling in their background; the relationship with counseling opens doors to employment or even other opportunities, but they are still art therapists.

Now I am a professor in an art therapy program. In this role, I have come to understand that some art therapists have identity concerns. Students are immensely curious and yet anxious about their newly chosen profession. They want to feel confident that their new identity will be embraced by the real world of education and medicine, as well as mental, community, and public health. They want to be employable. In deference to all the art therapy students across the globe, I take on the challenge to parse apart the issue of identity.

Early Identity Battles

Establishing and consolidating a professional identity takes time in any profession. It may be especially difficult in art therapy, because of the inevitable tug of war between the clinician's artist-self and therapist-self. (Rubin, 1999, p. 129)

Every new profession faces identity conflicts. The field of art therapy is no different. It is commonly known that numerous battles over the identity of the art therapist and the profession of art therapy were fought in the early days of the profession in the United States. *Art as therapy* and *art psychotherapy* were the two prevailing perspectives of the profession in the 1960s and 1970s. Although this duality seems simplistic today, it was not in those early days. One aspect of these heated encounters was centered on the *purpose* of art in therapy. The fight about these two perspectives was also about where and how we worked. If we wanted to be seen as part of the psychiatric, psychological, clinical world and if we were to be regarded as primary therapists, art psychotherapy was the identity to be touted (Naumburg, 1966). If we wanted the healing value of art to be the emphasis of our work, then art as therapy was primary (Kramer, 1971). There is no doubt that this struggle was weighty, important, and timely. A secondary concern underlining this dichotomy was the question, *Are we artists or are we therapists?* Early practitioners were flummoxed about this question, and debates at conferences were contentious with the answers being equally difficult and contentious (Rubin, 1999).

Refining the Debate

Today, this *either/or* debate is outdated because art therapists now work in such a variety of settings that the issue is almost moot. As a profession, we advocate for art therapists to work in a wide spectrum of settings. By default, if we proffer that art therapists should be able to work in any number of settings, we have to let go of the notion that there is an *either/or*.

Each of us has our own grandmothers and grandfathers, mothers and fathers, as mentors, teachers, heroes, and heroines. I am intrigued as I listen to art therapists speak of their teachers and supervisors and how these revered individuals shaped their notion of their work and their identity as art therapists. Because of all these mentors, art therapists have honed their individual view of the field and their own way of working. But we are all still art therapists.

We also know our role when working with clients depends on *their* needs and not on whether one advocates for art psychotherapy or art as therapy. Treating a non-verbal, frightened child, I might begin with engaging her or him in simple art processes, painting simple shapes or objects, rolling clay snakes, and enjoying the feel of various pieces of cloth to make a simple quilt. Only after rapport is built can I assist the child in deepening the understanding of a particular art object. The reverse may also be part of a treatment plan; art content may be questioned directly, and only later the client is encouraged to explore various media as deemed therapeutic by the art therapist.

That Was Then, This Is Now

In 2013, I sit in my university office amazed that questions about our professional identity are still with us. Identity battles made sense in the 1970s and 1980s, but we have not only entered a new millennium, we are also in an era where art as part of healing is widely accepted. Are there forces around us that make us question our professional identity? More to the point, are there internal influences that keep us deliberating this question? Automatically it comes to mind that external forces may be at the root of this questioning. But I am thinking there may be something about our profession or something about us as art therapists that keeps us questioning our identity. In the next section, I examine both external and internal forces that may be fueling the identity question.

External Forces

As stated, it is easy to acknowledge that external forces keep us thinking about our identity. First, students report that they are asked by parents and friends to explain art therapy. Although these students have already embraced the identity of an art therapist even before completing the master's program, this questioning does have an impact. After 30 years of interviewing students for the art therapy program, I still hear:

> *I have always loved art and working with others. When an advisor or career counselor told me about art therapy, I just knew that it was for me. I may not previously have had the term for it, but I am meant to be an art therapist. I realized that I have used art for my self-therapy most of my life.*

Although the concept of art as healing has been around for millennia, art therapy as a profession is still relatively new. The tedious process of informing others, including other mental health professionals, about our profession can only help us solidify an identity.

In the art therapy master's program I have the honor of working in, we ask students to define art therapy in their own words—to own it—so that when they discuss their profession with others, they not only have the words but can define the profession with dignity and integrity. They get lots of practice explaining and demonstrating art therapy to other students and mental health practitioners. We ask them to do at least one in-service program at an internship site, and we do mock job interviews so they can learn to communicate about art therapy to prospective employers. These simple assignments push forward the notion that students can articulate key aspects of the profession and are capable of performing educative and public relation tasks. More importantly, these projects help to consolidate professional identity.

Second, we want to be equal partners at team meetings and be respected by team members, yet there is concern that physicians, psychologists, social workers, counselors, and other related professionals will keep us away from the table. Sometimes the tension and urgency to move ahead and move *now* just to keep up with others is palpable. Of course we live in an ever-changing world, and we need to be realistic about our place in the mental health world, but is the panic necessary? Having art therapy professionals who are good at their job will eventually ameliorate this. Public relations can't and won't be done overnight.

Third, perhaps it is a problem of credentialing. In our not-so-recent past, credentialing art therapists was a divisive concept, but external forces pressured us to develop a credential that had "teeth." Thus, the development of a credentialing exam took shape. Many art therapists were concerned that reducing art therapy to "testable" constructs might belittle what we do as professionals. Today. most art therapists understand the need for a strong credential even if they do not accept the paradigm whole-heartedly. Credentialing bodies are responsible for delineating the art and practice of a particular profession. For example, the ATCB continuously monitors the practice of art therapy so that the credentials offered to art therapists have weight and meaning behind them. I have only worked with this body peripherally, yet I have witnessed its dedication to understanding all aspects of the profession of art therapy as well as identifying all the skills necessary to practice art therapy. Once one identifies and understands all these skills, it is impossible not to acknowledge that we are a profession.

Now that we have a strong credential, I wonder why obtaining the ATR(c) [Art Therapist Registered] or the ATR-BC© [Board Certified and Registered Art Therapist] has not strengthened one's identity as an art therapist. Why has this not happened in our profession as it has in related professions? I do not have definitive answers to these questions, but in my experience, alumni of the graduate program with which I am affiliated write or call when they receive their ATR©. They are thrilled when they pass the credentialing exam. Even before graduation, students are finding credentialed art therapists to supervise them and excited when they find employment so that they can begin to work toward professional credentials.

Fourth, the question of identity may have shifted recently to be about whether we are art therapists or counselors who use art. For some new art therapists, this is not a problem, but if one's degree title is art therapy yet the license held is counseling,[1] the identity waters can get muddy quickly. Most states offer licenses to professionals in therapy fields. Few states offer an art therapy license; in others, art therapists can qualify for a license with related professions. If one resides in a state that does not have an art therapy license, it makes pragmatic sense to seek out a license in a related field. In this environment of professionalism and accountability, it is unassailable practice that many employers and agencies want to employ a therapist who holds a license. There is a check and balance of professional integrity that accompanies a license. But if I am a credentialed art therapist who holds a counseling license in the state in which I live, does this make me less of art therapist? Does this confuse my identity?

To begin to answer this question, Feen-Calligan (2012) interviewed graduate students in a counseling and art therapy program as well as graduate students in an art education and art therapy program about their professional identity. At the program where Feen-Calligan conducted this research, art therapy education is under another degree title. Using a phenomenological approach to the interview process, Feen-Calligan found that the majority of the students "described their professional identities as a combination of art therapy, counseling, and

---

1. As stated before, currently most art therapy graduate programs do not offer a degree called "Art Therapy." Also, to my knowledge, Florida does not require a license to practice art therapy.

teaching" (p. 152). These students could not separate their identity as either an art therapist or a counselor.

Because I work in a program where the degree title contains "art therapy," the concern over identity may not be as pronounced as with other graduating art therapists. When working with students, I want to hear about their vision of art therapy and learn about their interests regarding with whom they want to work. Discussions around the type of art therapist they want to become take front and center. But there is rarely any concern about their identity as an art therapist. Thus, would the results of Feen-Calligan's survey be different if the degree title was art therapy and where the student took a few additional counseling classes in order to be eligible for a counseling license? Would their identity be more singular?

Feen-Calligan's results make sense given that her research participants' degree title is either counseling or education, where art therapy is a specialization under these degree titles. One could speculate that the results might be different in programs where the degree title is art therapy and students take the extra requisite courses to qualify for a counseling-type license in their state. Clearly, more research on this topic is necessary.

Internal Forces

Rubin (1999) used the term *shame dynamic* (p. 130), to describe how expressive arts therapists sometimes view themselves. Fearing that we are the poor stepsisters of the mental health world may keep us looking outward for recognition and positive reinforcement rather than looking inward to consolidate and strengthen our professional identity. With shame there is continuous questioning about who we are. I can see this happening today. From my perspective, the frequent questionings in our newsletter and journals may actually fuel insecurity about professional identity.

There also seems to be a culture of bitter debate with each new step toward identity solidification. Are we so afraid to be clearly touting our art therapy identity? To let our art therapy flag fly? Without squashing differences in perspectives, I think we, as a profession, need to realize that we are all heading in the same direction, and we have similar goals. We may not want to take the same road to where we are going, but we all have an aim that is clear: We want to advance our work. I hope we do not allow negative internal forces to get in our way of identity consolidation.

Art Therapists' Identity as Researchers

Looking at important issues through an either/or lens may have spilled over into how we view other aspects of the profession, including research in the field. Should art therapists be researchers and, if so, what types of research should we be conducting? At AATA conferences, panels of researchers asked these questions and tried to provide some guidance. Nonetheless, two factions emerged in the 1980s and 1990s. Researchers interested in studying the efficacy of art therapy and with which types of patients and clients were advocates of quantitative research. Those in the quantitative camp worried that a body of evidence was needed to ensure that what we did was effective. Others were more interested in how art therapy works and promoted qualitative research. Some qualitative researchers expressed concerns that quantitative research was only for convincing other professionals that art therapy was valid and effective. Others realized that art therapists also need to be informed about what art media and art therapy theoretical perspectives as well as techniques are best used with various individuals.

Throughout the 1990s, the battle for the hearts and minds of new art therapists to select a research side seemed to deepen. Thank goodness for researchers who touted the need for both types of research. Today, arts-based and mixed methods are in vogue and are useful to our profession. The issue now is that we need more research. Critical issues need to be examined using rigorous and sound methodologies that are congruent with the research question. Many new and emerging art therapy researchers are hard at work attempting to answer important questions in our field.

Doctoral Education and Professional Identity

In 1993, I was a research partner with Lusebrink and Campanelli on a study about art therapists with doctoral degrees. We wanted to uncover the types of doctoral programs art therapists had attended as well as the topics and research methods used for their dissertations. It was interesting to note that of 78 art therapists who responded to the survey, 16 various degree programs were held, ranging from psychology and art education to health administration. Eight reported that *art therapy* was in the name of the degree title. Although there were no art therapy doctoral degrees at that time, these individuals attended the Union Institute, where they had the freedom to frame both (a) their programs of studies, and (b) the degree title.[2]

When this research was conducted 20 years ago, the integrity of the professional identity of these doctoral-level art therapists was in question, especially because the majority of degree titles were in related fields not in art therapy. Two outcomes from the survey might help to verify that identification with art therapy was paramount. First, all but eight held the ATR credential, which implied these doctoral-level art therapists "had at least one year of clinical experience beyond the master's degree prior to beginning doctoral studies" (Lusebrink, Rosal, & Campanelli, 1993, p. 233). Second, both qualitative and quantitative research methods were used by the doctoral-level art therapists and the authors surmised that this "reflected the dual nature of *our* field as being from both behavioral sciences (quantitative focus) and fine art (qualitative focus)" (p. 233, italics added).

Today, there are a few university doctoral programs that do have art therapy in the degree. As the profession begins to embrace doctoral-level work more fully, it will be interesting to see how the professional identity issue gets framed by the professionals who hold these advanced degrees. Doctoral students must engage with research. With more research, perhaps we can finally put identity concerns to rest.

Conclusion

I value my profession, my colleagues, and all the work that has been done over the decades to advance our profession and identity. I am amazed and excited about our professional progress. Although debate over professional identity is important, I wish to see us couch the debate more delicately. I want all of us to think about ourselves as art

---

2. Things have changed at Union, and attaining a doctoral degree called "Art Therapy" is no longer possible. As far as I know at this time, there are no U.S. doctoral degrees specifically pertaining to art therapy: Lesley University's degree is "Expressive Therapies" (a PhD with dissertation), Drexel University (formerly Hahnemann Medical College) is "Creative Arts Therapy"(PhD with dissertation), and there is a "Professional Doctorate" (DAT) at Mt. Mary's College, which is "Doctor of Art Therapy," with no dissertation required.

therapists first and foremost. Some of us may create more art than others, some of us may do more research than others, and some of us may be more of an educator than others, some of us may be more inclined to use more art or, conversely, more verbal clinical skills in therapy sessions than others. But these differences do not mean that any of us are lesser art therapists than others. Nor do these differences mean that the profession is disintegrating. If the debate continues, let it be a reasoned one based on evidence like that provided by Feen-Calligan (2012). Then we can argue, among other issues, the merits and consequences of dual training on professional identity with thoughtful discourse.

References

Feen-Calligan, H. (2012). Professional identity perceptions of dual-prepared art therapy graduates. *Art Therapy: Journal of the American Art Therapy Association, 29*(4), 150–157.

Kramer, E. (1971). *Art as therapy with children.* New York: Schocken Books.

Lowenfeld, V. (1957). *Creative and mental growth* (3rd ed.). New York: Macmillan.

Lowenfeld, V., & Brittain, W. L. (1970). *Creative and mental growth* (5th ed.). New York: Macmillan.

Lusebrink, V., Rosal, M., & Campanelli, M. (1993). *Art Therapy, Journal of the American Art Therapy Association, 10*(4), 226–234.

Naumburg, M. (1966). *Dynamically oriented art therapy: Its principles and practice.* New York: Grune & Stratton.

Naumburg, M. (1973). *An introduction to art therapy: Studies of the "free" art expression of behavior problem children and adolescents as a means of diagnosis and therapy.* New York: Teachers College Press.

Rubin, J. (1999). *Art therapy: An introduction.* New York: Taylor & Francis.

ART THERAPY IDENTITY

Judith A. Rubin, PhD, ATR-BC, HLM

For me, being an *art therapist* fits comfortably in a way that being an artist, an art teacher, a psychoanalyst, or a psychologist never has, even though I have been all of those at various times in my life. *Artist* was how I thought of myself through college, where I majored in art. I soon recognized I wasn't talented enough to be successful in the competitive world of fine art, and I feared I would not like commercial art. I considered getting a Ph.D. in art history because an art major at Wellesley required an equal number of hours in history, which was fascinating. Although I still find museums as appealing as when I discovered them in my teens, and they are truly a "home away from home" wherever I travel, I realized that I preferred working with people. I had offered a summer art class on our porch and later enjoyed being an arts and crafts counselor at camps.

Art teacher was how I saw myself when I finished graduate school in education. Sadly, while I thoroughly enjoyed teaching art, I ran into a number of problems in both Cambridge and Pittsburgh. I was young and naïve and didn't realize I was offending other teachers as well as principals and supervisors by rearranging classroom furniture, rejecting stencils and a paddle for discipline, and showing slides that were not in the prescribed curriculum. I eventually realized that I didn't fit into the world of public education in the late 1950s. Yet when I stumbled into art therapy in 1963, I knew right away that I had found my calling, even though it was early in the development of the profession. The elements that appealed to me then are still central: offering art as a way to help people go on growing, an endlessly fascinating challenge. Making it possible for children to discover themselves by finding their own artistic language had always been pleasurable. But the added component of helping them overcome obstacles, and thereby gain increased personal freedom, made art therapy even more satisfying.

I was extremely fortunate because my job title was always "art therapist," beginning in a psychiatric hospital in 1963, then at an outpatient clinic, and back to the same hospital, until I went into private practice for 11 years before retiring from clinical work in 1996. Any income since then has come from writing a book, giving a talk, doing a workshop, supervising, consulting, or serving on a thesis committee, but the topic has always been art therapy. Although I have revised most of my books since retiring, teaching about art therapy during the past 17 years has been primarily through filmmaking.

I made several 16 mm films during the 1970s and 1980s, inspired by my friend and colleague Fred Rogers with whom I worked for three years during the 1960s as the Art Lady on his television program "Mister Rogers' Neighborhood." Fortunately, my drama therapy colleague and I had formed a nonprofit in 1985 when we left the psychiatric hospital (where we led a Creative & Expressive Arts Therapy department) in order to be able to take our films and videotapes with us, and Expressive Media (EMI) has provided a home for the continuing production of films and sponsorship of educational programs on art and other expressive therapies. I have enjoyed learning how to edit on a computer; indeed, the creative part of filmmaking is as gratifying and addictive as painting used to be.

My own identity as an art therapist has always felt stable, although I may be kidding myself. I have always thought that the issue of art as therapy versus art *in* therapy or art *psycho*therapy was a false dichotomy. I think a competent art therapist is true to both *Art* and *Therapy* and puts them together in a way that seems best suited to meet the needs of whomever they are serving at the moment. I first wrote about this in 1978:

> Helping, like growing, can take many forms. Helping [a person] to grow through art can involve giving, showing, or telling. It may also mean watching, and often, waiting. Many times it means moving in, doing or saying something in an active way. At other times it means being present but silent, respectful of the other's primary absorption in the creative (versus the human) dialogue. Helping means many different things, but always it means being tuned into the other person—behaving in a way which respects their right to their own space, and makes it possible for them to gain control and freedom within it. (Rubin, 1978, p. 17)

My own understanding of "art therapy" is that it refers broadly to understanding and helping a person through art, and that it encompasses a wide variety of dimensions. These include the integrative aspects of the creative process, as well as the use of art as a tool in the service of discharge, uncovering, defense, or communication.

Art for any individual can and does become different things at different times. I find it impossible to characterize the process, even with one human being or in one setting as being any one thing alone or always. Rather, it seems that for anyone, the art activity over time ranges from being central and integrative to peripheral and adjunctive and back again, serving many different possible functions.

What is important to know is what is occurring when it is happening, and to have some sense of its meaning and function for that person at that moment in time. What seems equally vital to me is that the worker have the flexibility and openness to permit the individual to flow in different directions over time and the wisdom and creativity to stimulate, unblock, or redirect the flow when necessary (Rubin, 2005).

I am therefore not sure what is meant by the phrase "umbrella with many definitions" because I believe that you have to be flexible in how you approach each clinical/creative challenge. Art, therapy, and the interface where they meet are the inextricable elements in art therapy, whether the metaphor for the many possible clinical approaches is umbrella, basket, or continuum (Rubin, 2011a).

Perhaps what is meant by the various modes under the *umbrella* are the different terms with which art therapists describe their work. Knowing diverse ways of understanding human beings (theories of psychology) and theories for helping people grow (theories of psychotherapy) is useful because different folks really do require different strokes. Eventually, most art therapists settle on one well-understood and compatible model while maintaining flexibility in their work. Other essential aspects of responsible art therapy are, I believe, respect, discipline, and humility (Rubin, 2001).

Do You Have to Be an Artist to Be an Art Therapist?

While this is a legitimate question, I believe that the glorification of the practicing/exhibiting artist may have contributed to identity confusion among art therapists. It is indeed vital to have experienced the struggle of a genuine creative process, but I don't agree that it is essential to invest a lot of time, money, and energy unless it is a *calling* that cannot be ignored. I have many art therapist friends for whom this is true, and I respect the power of their passion to create.

I, however, gradually did less painting as I became increasingly invested in learning to be a better art therapist. I think that doing any kind of therapy is a fundamentally creative endeavor, continually challenging, and overwhelmingly responsible. The ethical component makes it a different sort of activity than painting or drawing, where the only person I need to please is myself. Doing art therapy requires me to be aware of the impact of everything I say or do on the life of another. That alone is humbling, and to safely effect change requires considerable creativity on the part of the clinician. It is best if done sensitively and *artistically*–that is being an artist as a therapist.

Helpful Questions

The Author/Editor asked contributors: *What would it take for art therapy to move past the duality/dialectic models of psychology/art, Naumburg/Kramer of the past which . . . imply adversarial right/wrong, into a less competitive model?* Both Naumburg and Kramer understood human beings and the process of change through Freudian psychoanalytic theory, although Naumburg was most influenced by early models of the mind regarding the importance of insight and making the unconscious conscious. Kramer's ideas were influenced by later developments in ego psychology, especially developing the capacity to manage unconscious forces via mechanisms such as symbolization and sublimation.

Having studied psychoanalysis for 10 years and teaching since 1983 at the Pittsburgh Psychoanalytic Center, my own opinion is that these two sets of ideas have never been mutually exclusive. Understanding is important, but so is being in charge of one's urges and anxieties. They are intertwined, and all it would take to correct any confusion is for art therapists to comprehend the relationship between these two aspects of growing well enough to not feel compelled to choose one or the other as "right."

Regarding *art therapy's place in mental health, education, and rehabilitation,* I worked in medical settings for most of my career but never felt that I was following the same "medical model" as my colleagues in the Department of Psychiatry in which I have taught since 1974. Art therapy has always been able to contribute to understanding what's "wrong" with people and, even more significantly, identify and harness what's "right."

Elements of education are found in all effective therapies, and "clinical" doesn't mean abandoning art, which is the aspect of our field's identity that is essential, central, and unique. Indeed, in the early years of the profession's development, practitioners in mental health settings needed to speak an informed clinical language that would be understood by psychiatrists, psychologists, and social workers. Similarly, art therapists in schools needed to speak in educational terminology. Knowing *DSM*[1] classifications is still necessary in mental health, whereas while in special education, art therapists need to be familiar with behavioral objectives and IEPs.[2] Rather than fostering identity confusion, this facilitates communication and collegiality

Is Art Therapy a Mental Health Discipline?

I believe the answer to this question is "Yes" because art therapy is concerned primarily with social and emotional well-being. As such it can and should be available in a wide variety of settings, from schools and community centers to shelters, nursing homes, clinics, hospitals, and hospices–anywhere that people can benefit from art's therapeutic potential.

Unlike speech therapists, who treat specific conditions, we don't treat anyone's art. Our goal is to help people improve their quality of life regardless of whatever trauma or developmental impasse they may have experienced and despite any disabilities they may have. Whether the art therapy is in a residence for those with Alzheimer's disease, an outpatient psychiatric clinic, or a school for the blind, the common purpose is to improve the person's mental state so that they feel better about themselves and can live life to the fullest degree possible. If becoming a competent artist accomplishes that goal, art therapists often help people develop skills that can be life-changing (Rubin, 2012). If they need to be able to assert themselves or overcome the effects of a preverbal trauma, art therapists can help to reach those objectives as well (Rubin & Irwin, 2010).

Of course art therapy has powerful educational and rehabilitative effects because creating art is rewarding in both internal and external ways. That is why artists-in-residence or art educators can have con-

---

1. *DSM* is the *Diagnostic and Statistical Manual of Mental Disorders* published by the American Psychiatric Association. Since 1952, when the first edition was published, it has served as the classification of mental disorders and has come to be the "language" of mental health practitioners, facilities, and health insurance.
2. IEP, the "Individualized Education Plan," is the legal term that school systems use to create a plan for a student with special needs. They do not use the *DSM.*

siderable therapeutic impact on people in hospitals, schools, and community centers. I hope that there will be more of them in the future, just as I hope there will be more art therapists. There will never be enough art-givers to meet all societal needs. But beyond being an art-giver, someone who understands diagnosis and therapy and is well trained clinically to observe and behave thoughtfully brings yet another kind of skill.

I recently had occasion to hear what an experienced art therapist "saw" in the behavior and artwork of a dear friend currently in an institution for those with dementia. The task the art therapist set for the group (to represent how they were feeling) was a targeted intervention designed to help them express something that wasn't being invited elsewhere in their program. The art therapist's observations of my friend's artwork, as well as her verbal and nonverbal behavior, were psychologically sophisticated and could not have been made by even a very empathic artist or teacher. Some art providers would be able to respond supportively, which would be "therapeutic," but they would not be as capable of helping my friend verbalize her anxieties and anger reflected in her drawing or to clarify a confused, distressed perception of her living situation.

The American Art Therapy Association's Role in Identity

The American Art Therapy Association's (AATA's) early contributions to art therapy identity were major. This professional organization identified the core components of individual competence, as well as the essential elements of an art therapy education. It was absolutely critical not to let others define art therapy, especially initially. Hammering out art therapy's identity through the development of professional standards (for Registration) and standards for training (curricular guidelines and, later, an approval/accreditation process for educational programs) allowed us to clarify the synthesis of art and therapy for ourselves and thus for others.

As often happens, however, as professions and their organizations mature, AATA's initial flexibility about individual routes to registration or methods of training was soon overtaken by what I believe to be an unhealthy and excessive degree of definition and rigidity. I sometimes wonder whether the continuous argument between apparently incompatible definitions of art therapy has been exacerbated by the very rigidity that may have led to a loss of the creative spark that animated the pioneers. Perhaps it is simply a normal evolutionary process.

It is a difficult balancing act to be sure, but I believe that we lost our way to some extent in the process of working toward recognition. Board Certification was never meant to assess clinical competence but was rather a route to licensure. That goal also led to the incorporation of counseling or marriage and family therapy in training programs. Clearly, it was a smart political move because the majority of art therapists currently practice under some sort of counseling license, and because our numbers remain far too small—only a few states have art therapy licensure. As a means to an end (employment, healthcare reimbursement), it was realistic, but it has further confused the already blurry issue of identity. Perhaps more distressing for the growth of the field, it has led to diminished identification with the professional organization AATA; this is also understandable but regrettable.

Is the AATA Mostly Competitive or Mostly Cooperaive?

This question is hard to answer because AATA has been both depending on the times, the pressures, and the leadership. One thing it has failed to be is *expansive,* and I believe that has been a terrible loss for the profession. That the membership numbers plateaued at around 5,000 and have grown only slightly in recent years is sad, and that students don't always join AATA is a loss for them and the organization.

I have visited many different state associations and have observed that some have been able to sustain the mutually supportive spirit that pervaded AATA in the early years. While people disagreed radically on many issues, with arguments often lasting late into the night, there was a sense of common purpose that allowed passionate disputes while retaining mutual respect and affection. Perhaps it is an inevitable effect of becoming an older and larger organization run by employees rather than volunteers, but the feeling of community is not as strong as before. For my generation, AATA was our extended family, our tribe. We felt close to each other, the kind of bond that exists among blood relatives (Rubin & Arrington, 2009). Recent generations have been less fortunate.

In the beginning, students were encouraged to join the AATA, and there was even a student representative on the Executive Board of the organization. Young professionals were eager to participate, and their energy was valued. I wish the AATA would actively encourage student chapters (some universities have them, but most do not) and that local art therapy chapters (a healthy development) should be even more closely tied to the national association. It is distressing to hear from talented colleagues of less than supportive treatment by AATA and their consequent disenchantment. Indeed, too many dedicated folks have been hurt over the years, and too few apologies have been offered. Some recent changes at conferences, such as everyone not automatically attending opening and closing receptions, have further worsened the situation.

Another major mistake in my opinion was separating ATCB[3] from the AATA. (Yes, I know why it was done.) The result is that many practicing art therapists for obvious economic reasons choose to pay dues to one and not the other. The fact that more than 2,000 credentialed art therapists do *not* belong to their primary professional association is an inevitable effect of the separation. This means that when the AATA represents the profession to anyone (government, employers, funders), it can speak only for members, who are a minority of trained art therapists. There are probably more than 10,000 art therapists by now, but there are only 5,000 members of the national professional organization.

The Role of Art Therapy Education

Schools that encourage and support *student chapters* are helping more with identity than those that don't. Faculty who are secure, not feeling inferior to other professionals, naturally instill more self-esteem in their students. Thankfully, the current crop of art therapy educators is less likely to feel competitive with others because of loyalty to the field's founders who were often earlier educational program directors. The growth of Ph.D. programs is another hopeful development.

I believe that the AATA's primary responsibility is publicly defining art therapy, one shared with those who have written the books and led

---

3. The Art Therapy Credentialing Board registers and credentials art therapists. It is a separate organization from the AATA. Originally, art therapy "Registration" (ATR) was accomplished through the AATA. When BC (Board Certificati) was originated, as I remember, these functions needed to be legally separated from the AATA, and a new organization was established.

the training programs that have helped to define the field. Additionally, every art therapist is responsible for defining and moving the field forward because each is asked by employers, clients, and others what art therapy is.

Sharing with Other Caregivers

How can art therapy be open and "welcoming" to others (e.g., "teach" others how to do it and still portray itself as something special and different)? I have never understood this anxiety except as a turf issue. Child therapists use art, whether they call themselves play therapists, child life specialists, child psychiatrists, child psychologists, or child analysts. We do not own art any more than we own therapy, and we never have. What we have that is unique is a deep understanding of both art and therapy and sufficient expertise in putting them together to be able to do so most effectively, whether for assessment or treatment. I believe it is essential to be open and welcoming to others who want to use art for understanding and helping, whether they are nurses, psychiatrists, special educators, or artists. In this way, a professional art therapist is an educator as well as a clinician.

Inevitably, any profession will attempt to articulate its own identity, but others will have their perceptions of it as well. There is no question that art therapists are defined in both ways. However, the profession needs to take responsibility for clarifying and correcting others' perceptions whenever that seems appropriate, and to do so as generously as possible. I believe we have nothing to lose by being *inclusive* and much to lose if we are *exclusive.*

We have been amazingly successful because the idea of "art therapy" is known in a way that it was not when I began in 1963. That cuts both ways, however, because, as in the early days of the field, any artist or volunteer working with a disabled population or in a treatment setting (hospital, prison) might see themselves as doing "art therapy" or can be perceived by others as an "art therapist." The discipline is now in a stronger position than ever before, when art therapy was often seen as a frill and not a serious endeavor. But I believe it is also even more compelled now to clarify the similarities and differences between art therapists and those in related fields. I have tried to do that often (Rubin, 2005, 2009) and especially in the film *Art Therapy Has Many Faces* (2004).

The image of art therapy in the world today is positive and growing because art is more central in many cultures than in Western society where the profession began. Thus, the idea that art can be profoundly helpful to people who are suffering is compatible with most communities (Rubin, 2011b). To grow in a healthy way, I believe that in the future, art therapy needs not only to define itself ever more clearly but also to be more inclusive, to teach those in related fields to offer art more effectively to their patients or students, and to educate consumers and employers about the unique capacity of a trained art therapist to help those for whom words are not enough.

References

Rubin, J. (1978). *Child art therapy.* New York: Van Nostrand Reinhold.

Rubin, J. (Ed.). (2001). *Approaches to art therapy* (2nd ed.). New York: Routledge.

Rubin, J. (2004). *Art therapy has many faces* [DVD]. Pittsburgh, PA: Expressive Media, Inc.

Rubin, J. (2005). *Artful therapy* (3rd ed.). New York: John Wiley & Sons.

Rubin, J. (2009). *Introduction to art therapy: Sources & resources.* New York: Routledge.

Rubin, J. (2011a). *The art of art therapy* (2nd ed.). New York: Routledge.

Rubin, J. (2011b). *Art therapy: A universal language for healing* [DVD]. Pittsburgh, PA: Expressive Media, Inc.

Rubin, J. (2012). *Yes you can! Art therapy for people with disabilities* [DVD]. Pittsburgh, PA: Expressive Media, Inc.

Rubin, J., & Arrington, D. (2009). *Visionaries, pioneers & early settlers* [DVD]. Alexandria, VA: American Art Therapy Association.

Rubin, J., & Irwin, E. (2010). *Creative healing in mental health* [DVD]. Pittsburgh, PA: Expressive Media, Inc.

ART THERAPY IDENTITY

Gwendolyn McPhaul Short, MA, ATR-BC, CSC-AD

My personal identity with regard to art therapy is a sum total of my education, my experiences, and my relationships with many art therapists who have helped to shape the art therapist I am today. I entered a field I had never heard of and chose it because I could combine art and psychology and not have to choose between the two. In my family of origin, I was the first to go to college and the first to pursue a master's degree. Everyone knew I loved art, but to be able to go on and make it a major part of my career was pretty exciting.

My beginning years in art therapy were formed by what we would now call a "mentorship." One of my major influences was Nancy Schobel, whom I met when I interned as a graduate student at Prince George's County Hospital. We became fast friends and colleagues. Together, we traveled to the American Art Therapy Association (AATA) conferences, worked on presentations, and, on a more personal basis, shared family events. Nancy introduced me to camping, canoeing, gardening, making grape jelly, and doing basic home renovations. Together, we traveled domestically and abroad to Germany, Switzerland, and France. We were present at each other's weddings. All of this was in between actively working together on various committees in the Potomac Art Therapy Association and holding different positions, including president. All of this led to our working on committees for AATA–especially the Governmental Affairs Committee.

Nancy was elected to the AATA Board of Directors, which curtailed some of our traveling and rooming together at the conferences, but not our friendship. Nancy was a real go-getter and truly a woman before her time because the ideas and thoughts she had were ambitious but not unobtainable. I say "a woman before her time" because some of the things she envisioned are challenges that are still being worked on today. What I did not fully realize was that assisting her in her many endeavors was grooming me for more active roles in the AATA.

It was a tremendous blow to me when Nancy Schoebel died in 1990. My friend was gone, and I was numb because my world had been enriched by the relationship we shared. At some point, I realized that the best way to honor my friend was to forge ahead and continue working for the AATA. Nancy not only dreamed for herself, but she dreamed for me too. She often said, "Gwen, I see you teaching art therapy at Howard University someday." Because of Nancy Schoebel, I became involved in the AATA.

In Nancy's honor, I continued my work with the AATA. During the early years of the AATA, few people of color attended the conferences. Therefore, it was easy to "see" those who attended regularly and to form bonds with them. Little did I know at the time that Georgette Powell, Lucille Venture, Cliff Josephs, Sarah Mc Gee, Vivian Ware, and Charles Anderson were on a mission to recruit and, hopefully, retain new art therapists of color. But there was a strong feeling of support and encouragement among us, and we looked out for each other. If money was short, we shared what we had, and that made it possible for us to continue coming to the conferences. In years to come, I would learn about the greatness that I was in the midst of and didn't realize it at the time.

Friendships and Connections

My friendships with other art therapists-those who were people of color and those who weren't–helped form my identity. Working on committees and boards, establishing special projects together, and rooming at conferences helped create close friendships. The special bonds I formed with some of my classmates in the graduate art therapy program at George Washington University continued to flourish in my professional life afterward.

Along this journey through art therapy, there are other relationships that I treasure and know that they helped with my becoming the art therapist I am today. Charlotte Boston and I have grown close as we worked on many projects together, but most importantly AATA's Multicultural Committee for many years. Cheryl Doby-Copeland and I go way back to the early days of the AATA, but our friendship has grown more solid during the last decade. Working closely with Anna Hiscox, Stella Stepney, and many others has influenced me, and I am quite proud to call them my friends in the field. When I look on the horizon, I am truly impressed by some of our newcomers, and I know they are going to make marks on the field of art therapy like none others. They are propelling me into the IT world kicking and screaming, but it has to be done, so thank you Lindsey Vance and Martina Martin, to name a few.

The Multicultural Committee

I thank many past Multicultural Committee chairs who raised questions of who *were* the art therapists of color in art therapy. Jayshree George, Savneet Talwar, and Jordan Potash are a few who pushed for more information on them for the history of the committee. I was inspired by Linney Wix, who presented on Mary Huntoon[1] (whom I didn't know about), which made me want to research art therapy pioneers of color, who were there at the beginnings of the AATA but were not mentioned. We started with interviews of the living pioneers.

Anna Hiscox interviewed Cliff Josephs. Charlotte Boston researched Lucille Venture, the first PhD in art therapy with her dissertation, "The Black Beat in Art Therapy." Cheryl Doby-Copeland researched Sarah McGee. Ahead of her time, Sarah worked with migrant workers. Often her presentations were not accepted at the AATA conference, so she would present them and her videos in her hotel room. Charlotte and I interviewed Georgette Powell long ago and attempted to get the article published, but it was a journey of years before it happened. And that was because of Maxine Junge, who initiated a series on the art therapists of color in *Art Therapy, Journal of the American Art Therapy Association.* Jordan Potash interviewed Wayne Ramirez, one of the founding members of the Wisconsin Art Therapy Association, which was established prior to the founding of the AATA.

I had the task of researching Georgette Powell, one phenomenal woman. A prolific artist, activist, and founder and director of Tomorrow's World Art Center, where she provided services to teens and senior citizens for more than 30 years, Georgette held a massive arts festival annually, in Malcolm X Park, in Washington, DC.

Our research elicited many discussions and planning about what to do next. Finally after many years, and much help from Judy Rubin and Andrea Tree—who initially put the film together—"The Wheels of Diversity" was born. Needless to say, we all were elated beyond mea-

---

1. Mary Huntoon was a white woman who worked in Kansas and at the Menninger Clinic for many years. She was omitted from most histories of art therapy until my 1994 book (with Paige Asawa), *A History of Art Therapy in the United States.*

sure. It is sad that Sarah McGee, Lucille Venture, and Georgette Powell never had the opportunity to see themselves honored in this film, which will last for many years to come.

I have learned much from these individuals and others. I am sure I am an art therapist today because of the nurturing, guidance, and encouragement they provided me. A few of the most important lessons were: be strong, hold onto your beliefs, and you can accomplish whatever you set your mind to. Be steadfast in the desires of your heart, and never take your eye off the prize.

Work

Art therapy, however, does not fit with my employment. Still I feel it is incumbent on me to advocate for art therapy and show the administration of my facility what they are missing by not providing it to the citizens of Prince George's County, MD. I have been at the Prince George's County Health Department for 33 years; I have worked in the Partial Hospitalization Program (Adult Day Treatment), the Special Education wing of a local elementary school, and Community Outreach and Treatment Services (COATS) for the chronically mentally ill and homeless. I also worked in an intensive outpatient substance abuse treatment program for women and the Adult Drug Court. No matter where I worked, I brought my skills as an art therapist with me. Therefore, in all of these programs, when I was there, so was art therapy. *My employers knew about art therapy through me.* I knew the value of art therapy, and, at times, the administration allowed me to practice it. Ordering art supplies was evidence of their silent approval.

Then a miracle happened. After 30 years at the Health Department, my director said, "Gwen, we want you to be the art therapist for the Division of Addictions and Mental Health." I was honored, shocked, and oh so grateful to finally have the opportunity to be an art therapist. All I could say was "Can I have a county car to make the art mobile?"

I had complete control developing an art therapy program that covered the county and as many addictions programs as would have art therapy. This also allowed me the opportunity to have art therapy graduate students for internships, and, perhaps most importantly, I could introduce art therapy to the Division of Addictions and Mental Health. I knew that this would be a challenge because of the varied populations and the number of different programs in the Division. I was excited to take it on and immediately started contacting programs to meet with staff to do in-services so they had hands-on experience and a better understanding of what their clients would be exposed to in art therapy.

I contacted George Washington University's art therapy program to request an intern—a second-year graduate student who was a self-starter and an independent thinker. Over the years, I have been able to train a number of graduate students. We worked with children and adolescents in the youth programs, women in the Methadone Clinic, and the women and children's program. We worked in a special education class in a local high school, the Adult Drug Court program and the Juvenile Drug Court, with adolescents in group homes, and occasionally with individuals needing grief counseling. Participation in Health Fairs and Career Days at local high schools were some additional ways we continued to promote art therapy in the County. You see why the student had to be flexible and courageous enough to take on this huge task. We were quite successful and tried to meet all of the requests we received.

The euphoria lasted for two years, and then I was told I would be transferred again to another program. So much to my chagrin, the art therapy program would end. I tried everything I could think of to keep it going, even if it were not me, just to keep it going. I agreed to supervise students from afar and was told "no" because they could not observe me conducting art sessions. The clients we were able to work with were sorely disappointed. Many call me the "Art Lady" and continue to ask whether I am coming back. So maybe when I retire, I can go back and volunteer. Although I continue to approach the administration with the suggestion of hiring an expressive therapist (my preference is an art therapist, of course), maybe it might happen with the new art therapy licensure in Maryland.

In my private practice, art therapy fits quite well because that is why the client came to me. Although to have a small private practice was always a part of my lifetime goals, it came as an opportunity before I felt I was ready and earlier than I had anticipated. My friend Barbara Sobol (who had long since left Prince George's County) asked me to work with two youth who were in the care of Montgomery County residing in group homes. Both were foreign born but had lived in the

United States since their early years. One was a boy from Suriname, South America, and the girl was from Sierra Leone, Africa. This began a journey of two years with them meeting once a week. Together we went through school problems, illnesses, moving to different group homes, staff issues, graduations, relationships, the diagnosis of HIV, and marriage for one of them.

Barbara Sobol asked me to work with another troubled young man. He was also in a group home and a ward of Montgomery County. He was estranged from his family of origin, in his late teens, white, and intelligent, and he often delighted when he knew more than me. For two years, we met weekly; sometimes he loved me and sometimes he hated me. I was never sure of his true diagnosis, but certainly he could be outrageous. At the end of our work, he fired me because I would not comply with his disorganized thinking.

My practice was possible because Barbara referred clients to me and allowed me to rent space in her studio to work with them. So, what more could I ask for? This clearly was taking advantage of opportunity knocking on my door. My advice to anyone is always be ready because one never knows when the desires of your heart will present themselves.

Must an Art Therapist Be an Artist?

I don't believe arts therapists have to be artists, but they have to know art and the basic fundamentals of art. They need to know how to guide clients through art processes. If not, they cannot function as art therapists, which could lead to more harm than good. Presenting oneself as an art therapist without proper training could also cast a negative light on the field of art therapy.

What does making art have to do with personal/professional identity? I often say that art is the vehicle that brought me to art therapy, and seemingly it is the thing that I can easily set aside. I tell myself I'm too busy, I'm too tired, I'm too . . . one excuse after another. This is a terrible situation to be in, but it stems way back to when I was a student. I always had to work full time and went to school part time. The result was it took me eight years to complete undergraduate school. Then, facing graduate school, with the requirements and demands, my job at the time would not accommodate my new schedule. Thus, I had to resign my job of 10 years from the National Geographic Society.

Luckily, I was able to find a night job, from midnight to 8:00 am at the Prince George's County (MD) Hospital and Medical Center. I worked as a psychiatric intake worker in the Emergency Psychiatric Service (EPS). This allowed me to do practicum and internships during the day, art therapy classes in the evenings, and back to work at night. So doing my own art, which was ceramics, was put on hold.

Now art therapy master's programs consist of 48 to 60 hours and include art projects. Art can be wonderful. But art can also be stressful and/or a stress reducer. I have seen a major difference in the art therapy interns I was fortunate enough to work with. They were constantly busy with academic requirements and art projects. I always felt that made them keep their art current and readily available to them, so they could not set their art aside even if they wanted to. I could not have accomplished a graduate program years ago with the demanding schedule I had at the time. I thank God that I was able to become an art therapist when I did.

The American Art Therapy Association:
Cooperation or Competition?

Following are some thoughts about [the first professional organization] the American Art Therapy Association. In particular, I address the dominance in the AATA of cooperation or competition:

At this point in time, I consider the AATA to have been mostly cooperative. This happened because of the youthfulness of the field of art therapy. Certainly in the early days, AATA members often held vastly different ideas, but they all supported the idea of art therapy and cooperated together to drive it forward. Other fields have been around longer and set standards in their day. What is unfortunate is that because of this, younger disciplines like art therapy have often been under their shadow and have had to abide by their standards sometimes not creating its own.

When the AATA was establishing a Multicultural Committee, I remember consulting with the occupational therapy organization regarding their Multicultural Committee. I visited their building in Washington, DC, and met with the person in charge. Unlike in the AATA, in occupational therapy's professional organization, this was a paid position. The occupational therapy woman explained that it was her job to make sure there was some representation of diversity at conferences and in their journal. She described encouraging members to write, and even if they put their thoughts on a napkin, she could help with writing an article for their journal. Thus, she was able to promote the diversity in their organization.

The AATA was just starting to pay attention to multiculturalism, and this meeting with the occupational therapist was for information gathering. Later, when I served on the ATCB, I was charged with putting together credentialing exams for art therapy Board Certification. We did not know how to set up an exam and met with others to gain the knowledge needed to meet the goal of producing our own credentialing exam.

So in many ways, because of the youth of the AATA, we have had to be cooperative, particularly in our learning from more established mental health disciplines and the "outside world." Now that art therapy as a profession has grown and matured over the years, it is better able to assert itself in a more sophisticated manner.

AATA will need to be more competitive to those without training who say they are art therapists. Anyone can say they are an art therapist, and in the past, art teachers and artists, to name a few, have called themselves that. But are they really? Is *the public* protected if uncredentialed "art therapists" do harm under their self-proclaimed title? "Real" art therapists are highly skilled professionals with an investment of time and money in graduate education and practice. Their training and experience takes them to a different level of expertise than those, no matter how psychologically informed, who simply use art materials. If they cause harm or injury by not knowing exactly what they are doing, they can be negative to the field of art therapy as a whole. Therefore, it is incumbent on the AATA to defend itself whenever the need arises. In summary, the AATA has, in my opinion, evolved into a more competitive organization.

In What Way Does Current Art Therapy Education Contribute to or Make Identity Formation Difficult, and What Should it Do?

Art therapy master's-level educational programs are the vehicle to get an art therapist to the point of being able to deliver services based on knowledge and acquired skills. There is basic knowledge that every art therapist should know, and these standards are spelled out by the AATA. However, once the basics are acquired, how does the new art therapist obtain a job and begin practice with confidence? I have had art therapy interns who were quite knowledgeable but lacked confidence to go forward as clinicians. During the years after graduation, I strongly urge educational programs to provide support for novice art therapy practitioners.

With my student interns, I study the organizational chart for the Health Department we work in. It is important to know what the agency is all about. I introduce them to many of the key players on the chart. Interns need to know where they are spending a year of their learning time. They need to represent the agency to whomever they are working with at the time. One never knows—if a job comes available, someone may remember that meeting. Art therapy interns should always be prepared to market themselves *and* the field of art therapy. I ask interns to show me what they would do with the various populations we worked with and explain what was appropriate to do and what was not. Also, how they could make a task or technique workable for each population. Art therapy interns address treatment plans and write notes after the session to reflect on what was intended, what happened, and impressions of clients' progress or lack thereof. Mistakes are equally important to learn from, and even though I am the field supervisor, it is clear that I do not have all the answers, and I too make mistakes. We talk about it, we examine it, we dissect it, learn from it, and move forward.

It may be difficult for art therapy educational programs to actually help the students meld academics, acquire courage to work with clients, employ decision making and the finesse of being with the client, and ease into trusting themselves as therapists. But that is their job. I must also admit that I am not in the educational programs on a regular basis. I am a guest lecturer from time to time, teaching from my own experiences. But I do see uncertainty and self-doubt in some of the second-year students about to graduate, and it worries me.

Have I Done Enough to Open the Way for the New Generations of Art Therapists?

When students ask me at conferences who certain people are, I make it a point to introduce them to authors, board members, and "names" they have come across, and it does wonders for them. It is as if they are meeting celebrities, and that is important in helping them feel comfortable at the conferences and part of the profession. One time I walked through the hotel lobby where the AATA conference was held and saw a young lady sitting by herself looking sad. I approached her and asked what was wrong. She burst into tears and explained that her classmates had left her. I introduced her to some other young conference attendees, and she was fine after that.

When a group of students shared some poems they had written and published in the school newsletter, I was inspired. Four of them had written poems titled "I Am Not My Color," and the fifth one, an Asian student, read her contribution as well. They were awed when I introduced them to prominent art therapist Judy Rubin and even more so when she wanted to hear their poems. Thus, at a party in a hotel suite, we all huddled in the bathroom with some of them standing in the tub. It was an honor to share that moment with them as they read their poems to Judy, who was so receptive and encouraging to each one of them.

My philosophy is that I will never ask anyone to do something that I am not willing to do myself. When I encourage new art therapists to join committees, attend and present at conferences, write articles, attend the AATA Business meetings, and generally "make yourself visible," I can open a door. I say, "But you need to be ready to walk through it. If something is not right, speak up! I cannot advocate for you if I don't know the issues." This is my way of trying to keep talented young art therapists in the field, knowing that someday they will replace older generations and keep art therapy alive and prosperous. As a newly elected director on the AATA Board of Directors, I say, yes, you can achieve this as well.

My prayer and my question is that my journey through art therapy, the AATA, and the ATCB will not be in vain. I want to answer that looming question with YES, I have done enough! But there will be plenty left for the newer generations of art therapists.

Conclusion

In summary, I would describe my personal identity with regard to art therapy as strong, confident, open to new ideas, resilient, proud of my profession, an encourager, a mentor, an advocate, and a willing worker to advance the field of art therapy and pave the way for newer generations of art therapists. Currently, I sit on the AATA Board of

Directors elected by my peers. I look around at my Multicultural Committee members and say, "Yes, you can be here one day as well."

Art therapy has been my life. I can honestly say I have no regrets, and I will continue to cherish it. All in all, art therapy has served me well, and I can only hope that I am serving it well. I thank God that I was able to become an art therapist when I did, and I am grateful to all who have helped to shape me into the art therapist I am today.

WHAT IS ART THERAPY ANYWAY?

Harriet Wadeson, PhD, LCSW, ATR-BC, HLM

Before we can explore the identity of the art therapist, as this essay is intended to do, we must discuss what the art therapist does. In other words, what is art therapy?

Back in 1961, when I first entered the field of art therapy, people would ask me, "What is art therapy anyway?" I loved explaining this fascinating new work I was doing. After a couple years, however, I got tired of repeating myself and mostly brushed them off. These days, now more than 50 years since its beginning, people seldom ask because most people have heard of art therapy, although some are still confused and think of it as recreation therapy or work done only with children.

The answer to the question of what is art therapy is by no means a simple one. Although art therapy is a relatively small and young profession, it is amazingly diverse. Asking an art therapist what art therapy is may be akin to asking the six blind men to describe an elephant. Each is familiar with one part, the trunk that is like a snake, the ear that is like a fan, the rope-like tail, and so forth (Wadeson, 2000). Even though art therapy has its many nooks and crannies, I believe there are two main directions the field is taking presently: The first is based on a traditional therapy model, which is clinical in nature, and the second follows a more social service or community action format.

The clinical model is the one in which I grew up in my initial years of practice and research at the National Institutes of Health's (NIH)'s Institute of Mental Health (NIMH), where I worked for 13 years. I cut my art therapy teeth on work with adolescent patients who, though resistant to almost everything, found art making a way to express the difficult feelings they had trouble venting in any other way that was not explosive. For example, my patient Peggy expressed her fear of another patient's rage in a depiction of him moving from a storm to a fire (Wadeson, 2010).

I then worked for a number of years with psychotically depressed, often suicidal, patients and manic patients who had even more difficulty in expressing and dealing with their feelings. Despite extreme lethargy in some and manic disorganization in others, they too could

illustrate their feeling states in their art, such as the depression and suicidal feelings, about which one patient said, "You eat and you defecate,
and that's all there is to life" (Wadeson, 2010, p. 175). On occasion, I
even combined art therapy with other expressive modalities, such as
movement, music, and drama, to enliven these patients (Wadeson,
2010).

Most challenging was my work with acute schizophrenic patients.
Because they were hospitalized at NIMH primarily for research purposes, they were not medicated so that their schizophrenic condition
could be studied in its raw state uninfluenced by drugs. This was a rare
opportunity for me to come to understand schizophrenia, as patients
are typically medicated to rid them of hallucinations and delusions.
Most impressive to me about this condition was that these patients
existed in an envelope of isolation, buried in their own unique realities that were not shared by others. Nurses and nursing assistants on
the unit often told them to stop talking crazy. I, in contrast, asked them
to draw their hallucinations and delusions and to tell me about their
experience. Sometimes the artwork revealed continued psychotic ide-
ation after behavior seemed to indicate that it had cleared. But most
important, these patients were no longer alone in their idiosyncratic
worlds. Through artwork, I entered their worlds to the extent that they
would allow me. Craig, who was escorted to the hospital by seven po-
licemen and was considered dangerous, trusted me with his secrets in
his "Mother of the Universe." In this picture, Craig is held in the palm
of a giant hand.

Because NIMH is a research institution, I was expected to use art
therapy to produce research studies. This was a particularly interesting
challenge because an art production can provide raw data that remain
constant and can be observed. My research interest was to help illuminate the inner state of patients suffering psychoses (Wadeson, 2010).
During my tenure at NIH, I produced 27 papers on the subject, most
of which were published in psychiatric journals. So for me, a component of my clinical approach in art therapy was research into what the
art could tell about mental illness.

Along the way, I opened a private practice that enabled me to work
long term with clients, which often led them to make significant changes
in their lives. Particularly in the early days of my career, I would have
described the art therapy I conducted as a form of psychotherapy that

utilized art for self-expression and self-exploration, and, as such, my identity was one who combined art and psychotherapy in that way.

After directing an art therapy graduate program at the University of Houston for two years, in 1981, I moved to Chicago to establish an art therapy master's program at the University of Illinois (UIC). There was only a handful of art therapists in Chicago then, so as I visited various facilities to set up internships, I had to explain art therapy and describe how it might be useful to the facility's particular population. One thing I had in mind at this time was the expansion of the profession. I wanted to establish art therapy beyond its traditional venues of psychiatric hospitals, clinics, and schools for emotionally disturbed children. So I set up art therapy in homeless shelters, jails, aftercare centers, geriatric facilities, substance abuse treatment centers, and more. Others were thinking along similar lines as they developed art therapy in many kinds of non-clinical venues.

Obviously, the goals of the work with particular individuals, families, or groups would depend on the needs of the population involved. Often those needs were not of a clinical nature. For example, one of the early placements I set up for interns was a facility for developmentally delayed individuals at my university. At the end of the year, the clients hung an art exhibit of their work and celebrated with an opening reception. They knew I was their art therapist's teacher and couldn't wait to drag me over to their pictures and tell me all about them. Clearly, they had enjoyed making art and were proud of their accomplishments. Here the art gave clients a big boost in self-esteem rather than deep self-exploration (Wadeson, 2000).

Another example of this kind of art therapy is work in shelters for homeless people, many of whom have alcohol and drug abuse problems; this was established early in UIC art therapy training. The social and community aspect to this sort of work was apparent, where making art with others and displaying it together gives those who may feel isolated or rudderless a sense of community and purpose. Some of the groups of homeless women even participated together in making a banner to display in a local social justice demonstration. Some aftercare art therapy programs in the Chicago area developed by UIC graduates have been running for 25 years now. Many of their participants have utilized these services for years, in a sense making a home for themselves in them (Wadeson, 2000).

I am not sure what I would call this brand of art therapy, maybe community art therapy. I see it as being different from a more clinical model, although I see no reason that the two might not overlap at times. I think art therapists get themselves into trouble when they apply "either/or" definitions. I believe art therapy can embrace many ways of working, which need not compete with one another. I train my students to look at the needs of their clients and to be creative in designing art therapy services for them to meet those needs. Those needs may vary among different populations, from client to client, and even within the same client from time to time.

Given the great variety in the way art therapy is practiced with different populations, the question arises about how art therapists should be trained. With the present job market being as tight as it is today, I think art therapists are wise to learn to work with many different populations, rather than limiting themselves only to that group that currently captures their fascination. Obviously, no two-year master's degree training can encompass every possibility; therefore, I believe education should focus on *how* to think about the work, not just *what* to think. Art therapists should be trained to exercise their creative abilities in developing art therapy services, not just copy the successful efforts of their predecessors. Art therapy graduate study provides many opportunities for experimentation in the supervised practice.

In looking at the identity of the art therapist, I have concentrated on what art therapy is and the purposes it serves. I believe art therapists are defined by the work they do. But in developing the ideas for this book, Maxine Junge has raised some interesting questions about the person of the art therapist and the view of the profession as well. For example, she asks whether art therapists should be artists. Once again, I look to my own experience. "Harriet made art before it was fashionable," my mother used to brag. Nevertheless, there were dry periods in my life when I was working full time, going to school full time, and raising three small children all at once. Even so, I think I was doing good art therapy at those times. Perhaps it was because I had years of art making behind me.

During my cancer experience several years ago, when I was too sick to read or write, take a walk, or converse with a friend, I could make art. Through the six months of my cancer treatment, I made approximately 65 pieces of art. They helped get me through the effects of surgery, radiation, and chemotherapy. Creating art was a powerful antidote to my illness. (For a more complete description of what art making meant to me in the face of cancer, see *Journaling Cancer in Words and Images, Caught in the Clutch of the Crab* (Wadeson, 2011). Although I had used art making in the past to help me get through difficult experiences, I had never before immersed myself for so long a period in painting through my own adversity.

Does the power of this experience tell me that every art therapist should be an artist? I don't think so. But I do believe that to encourage patients and clients to make art and to find it meaningful, one must know that experience for oneself. I don't think a weekend art-making workshop will do it. Although I don't believe it is necessary to embrace the identity of artist, I do think it necessary to have had ongoing experiences creating art and deriving meaning from them.

Another question raised by Maxine Junge is how art therapy is viewed by others. Do we place ourselves among the "pantheon of mental health services" or are we more recreational/rehabilitative? I see no need to categorize our work in this way. *We are what we do.* Some art therapists do therapy. Some art therapists are community organizers. At times we are called on for crisis intervention, both for individuals and in community disasters. Art therapists have traveled to Haiti, New Orleans, and New York to tend to the emergencies there. We have many capabilities.

If we don't delineate ourselves, one might wonder how we can qualify for third-party health insurance payment. It seems to me that some of our work–that which is clearly therapy in a psychiatric or medical sense–should come under the umbrella of medical reimbursement. But many other forms of art therapy should not look to medical insurance for funding. Such work may be underwritten by grants from other sources, such as those obtained by social service agencies and organizations or schools. A one-size-fits-all approach definitely does not apply to the diversity in art therapy.

I have not come up with a clear-cut definition of either the art therapist's identity or even what art therapy is. But I have tried to explain art therapy as I see it today and the directions I see the field taking. On a more personal note, I have grown up with this profession. I started my career in art therapy when the field had barely begun, and I have watched it grow and develop beyond my imaginings. Art therapy has been my professional home, and art therapists are my professional family. That degree of familiarity makes definition difficult.

References

Wadeson, H. (2000). *Art therapy practice, innovative approaches with diverse populations.* New York: John Wiley & Sons.

Wadeson, H. (2010). *Art psychotherapy* (2nd ed.). Hoboken, NJ: John Wiley & Sons.

Wadeson, H. (2011). *Journaling cancer in words and images, caught in the clutch of the crab.* Springfield, IL: Charles C Thomas.

SUMMARY

The 21 previous essays can be considered "readings" about personal and professional art therapy identity by a range of art therapist writers and two students. Most essayists have been in the field for many years and have been both practitioners and educators. In the following summary, I establish the nature of this particular group of essayists–who they are–underscore some of their general themes and criticisms about professional identity, and highlight a perspective of difference.

Who Are They?

Although I invited representation in the group from art therapists with a variety of viewpoints, some declined to participate. While they may not appreciate that I categorized them, in my view, many of those who said "no" tended to be from what I assume to represent a main theoretical thrust of the field-art and the creative process as therapy. This particular focus is often represented in the book's essays, but rather than flowing from an overall theoretical focus, here it tends to be underscored as one *approach to art therapy practice,* the choice of which depends on the needs of the specific client or clients. Perhaps this is what it needs to be.

There are 21 essays and 22 writers. Most have been in the art therapy field for 25 years or more, some a great deal longer. Two were founders of the American Art Therapy Association, and four are called "Pioneer" art therapists, meaning that they have been in the field for many years and were there when the AATA was established in 1969. Six are current or past presidents of the AATA. Eight (of 22) hold the HLM[1] which is the highest award given in art therapy. Fifteen hold doctorates. Nine hold a state license in mental health discipline other than art therapy. All are "Registered Art Therapist" (ATR), and 15 are "Board Certified" (BC) Most have been or are art therapy educators.

Essayists describe their strong personal art therapist identities–many having been interested in art and psychology for years before

---

1. The "HLM" is "Honorary Life Member." It is voted on by the membership of the American Art Therapy Association and is awarded for extraordinary service to the profession.

they found the field. Issues of professional identity, however, are vastly more complex, confusing, and problematic for this group. Typical of inherent oppositional and even paradoxical approaches to practice were reflected in the emphases of Allen's "The Conscious Artist in Residence" and Gerber's "The Therapist Artist." What "comes first" is often a matter of individual choice rather than professional consensus or choice. Many mentioned an apparent lack of defined core values in American art therapy.

Themes of Professional Identity

While most writers believe that in its more than 50 years, the recognition of art therapy has grown and expanded tremendously, the ubiquitous question, "What IS art therapy anyway?" persists, and there is a good deal of confusion noted about what the difference is between a professional, trained art therapist, and someone who uses art techniques, such as an artist-in-residence or an art educator, who may call what they do "art therapy." Art is not the unique domain of art therapists, nor is it owned by them. Nonetheless, an educated and trained art therapist is a vastly different sort than someone who uses art as a technique. The confusion here is partly created by the internal challenges of the organized art therapy field and is partly an outgrowth that "art therapy" as it is known externally is so many different things. It needs to define itself.

As I consider it an indicator of American culture, I pay attention to the mentions of art therapy on TV. While the numbers of times it is mentioned have gone way up over the last 10 years or so, currently "art therapy" tends to be regarded as an *activity* therapy in an inpatient psychiatric setting. In TV episodes, art therapy looks a lot like an art class. On the show *Law and Order* and on *House* last week, a main character attended "art therapy class."

Initially, the mission of the American Art Therapy Association was to establish art therapy as an equivalent mental health discipline to psychiatry, psychology, and social work, with the master's degree being entry level to the profession. Some years ago, however, art therapy was placed as an "activity" therapy with a bachelor's degree as entry level on O'Net (an internet database supported by the U.S. Department of Labor/Employment and Training), which is a major source for all information about occupations. Currently, the AATA is attempting to change this placement to Code 21, which designates community and social services. Herein exactly lies the confusion and the challenge.

Following are statements representative of what essayists wrote about professional identity and art therapy. (The issues below, which tend to be quite critical, were all mentioned by essayists more than once, and some were described many times.)

Professional Art Therapy Identity

- We need to establish core common values and interests that can be maintained in all practice settings.
- I am afraid that at times we have lost sight of our core values.
- "I was unable to find a list of art therapy values."
- Consolidating a core set of values for art therapists is a challenge.
- "One could say that the profession doesn't have an identity but simply depends on whom one talks to . . . am I a person without a profession or a member of a profession reluctant to progress?"
- Art therapy remains *a field of practice* without a firm theoretical base.

Presenting Itself

- Art therapists have been too ready to adapt to trends and the dominant belief system.
- We need to be ourselves. We need to know what we believe and adopt that stance.
- We need to do a better job of "negotiating" with the external, regulatory world without compromising the integrity of the field.
- Polarization and competition within the field are outdated, as is a "right/wrong" stance.
- To move forward, *cooperation* within the field is needed.
- Unfortunately, the process of institutionalization has increasingly defined and rigidified standards of what art therapy is about.
- After initial flexibility, we are now at an unhealthy state of rigidity and definition. We have lost our way in the process of working toward recognition.
- We must create a climate of constructive debate in which differing ideas are not only accepted but embraced.

- We need a respect for individual differences and shared commonalities.

Education

- Dual identities are problematic for students and can lead to abandoning the art in art therapy after graduation. (A dual identity is when a student is attending an art therapy educational program but is also studying another mental health curriculum, and the degree often includes the "other" if it includes art therapy at all. This was originally established as an avenue for state licensing and, therefore, employment.)
- Art therapy education must be strongly connected to *employment* and "growing" employment. Education is of no use if a graduate art therapist cannot find a job with a living wage.
- Often there are far too many students educated for the numbers of available community jobs, which leads to anger and frustration on the part of many graduates. This doesn't do the profession any good.
- Art therapy master's education has become an industry of its own.
- Faculty members as teachers, mentors, and advisors are essential to instilling art therapy identity in students. They should have a healthy self-esteem about the profession and call themselves "art therapists."
- Are we afraid to be clearly proclaiming our art therapy identity?
- There should be student AATA chapters in education programs.

Must an Art Therapist Create Art?

- Jones: "Yes. I have always had an umbilical need and an attachment to the art world, to hold creativity dear."
- Rubin: "I believe that the glorification of the practicing/exhibiting artist may have contributed to identity confusion among art therapists."

The AATA

- There is a historical mistrust of the AATA.
- Mistrust of the AATA can lead to conspiracy theories and the fear that art therapy will be subsumed into a subgroup of the counseling profession.

- "I believe art therapy must leave the past behind and move forward, confidently."
- Possibly because of conflicting finances, AATA membership stays stable at about 5000. This means that the AATA can no longer say it represents all art therapists.
- The AATA needs to be more welcoming to students. Students should be able to attend yearly conferences at an affordable rate.
- Outreach to students by the AATA is essential.
- There should be a member on the Executive Board who represents students' viewpoints and is a student.
- The annual AATA conferences should be affordable to all, not simply those who have some institutional financial support to attend.

A Major Difference

Many art therapy writers in this book describe that a profession built on art, creativity, and difference has, in its understandable struggle for credibility and establishment of personal, professional, and educational standards, now become too rigid and representative of a kind of bureaucratic "sameness." Historically, American art therapy emerged within a psychodynamic worldview. It has expanded over the years and embraced a wide variety of approaches to practice with an ever-expanding breadth of clinical populations. Nevertheless, to establish a true profession, there must be more; there must be boundaries based on values and commonalities that differentiate it from other fields. Debra Linesch is one essayist who doesn't accept this concept of boundaries. In a provocative statement, she writes:

> I am someone who believes in the healing power of art in all areas of life.
> . . . Sometimes I'm not even sure there is a field called "art therapy."
> Perhaps this label is just another creator of arbitrary boundaries around
> processes that are complex, multi-layered and very difficult to categorize.
> After 30 years of practicing as an art therapist, the core values that make
> up my professional identity have more to do with an expansive belief
> in the meaning-making potential of the artistic process . . . perhaps there
> is no field called art therapy . . . no practice called art therapy . . . no
> job title called art therapist. Rather there is a way of approaching life.

Chapter 5

IDENTITY INITIATIVE, STEPS TOWARD A NEW DEFINITION: AN ACTION PLAN

In this chapter, I propose a two-year Action Plan to establish a shared art therapy public identity for the 21st century with the goal of enhancing the future of the profession and its sustainability. This plan considers important systems of the field, and although it may seem to be a series of consecutive steps, they do not need to be accomplished in order and, in fact, can be undertaken and accomplished concurrently. I have attempted to keep this Action Plan non-hierarchical and inclusive; all parts of the art therapy community must be heard from. American art therapy must retain its "specialness" while approaching the current cultural and political climate in a pragmatic manner. Trouble-shooting problems of organization and evaluation of the process will be done along the way. *Year one of the Action Plan is essentially discussion, establishing, and the coordinating of core values and important goals elements of professional identity. Year two is primarily for implementation and involves a broad public relations effort, beginning with the art therapy community itself.*

The language of a Final Product should be as specific as possible and include a plan for achieving the goals the profession sets for itself. A note about funding: Essentially, this is intended as a volunteer operation offering a unique opportunity for participants to contribute to the profession. Donations can also be part of the process, using internet websites such as "GoFundMe" and "Kickstart." It is highly recommended that this project should not depend on achieving a grant. The reason for this is, if any form of grant money is even available, it takes a long time—in fact, years. I believe a dedication to clarifying and establishing identity for the 21st century art therapy profession is urgent and should begin immediately

ACTION PLAN

Year One

Initiative 1: Conversation and Dialogue

Wherever art therapists come together, a dialogue about identity should begin.

1. **Coodinating group** of seven formed

   - Representation of all subgroups such as educators, students, the AATA, internet groups, practitioners, plus geographic diversity.
   - Work occurs via email, with an occasional conference call. Time commitment: meetings as needed through the year.
   - How to find group participants? Self-selected, plus ads in the AATA newsletter, journals, internet groups, and word of mouth.
   - Conference call to appoint two group members to act as "Co-Chairs."
   - Group members offer support and direction, as needed, to community dialogue and will coordinate information and action plans from the various groups.

2. Begin a broad-ranging dialogue about questions of professional identity across the art therapy community.

   - Small-group format (maximum of 10/group)
   - Including students, educators, practitioners, local organizations and AATA affiliates, the AATA and other art therapy organizations and blogs. A variety of advertising modalities should be used to reach as much of the community as possible
   - Time commitment: 1/month for a year (11 times)
   - Final product: Each group creates a two-page statement containing:
   (a) Core values, and

(b) Components of art therapy identity. Statement is submitted to the Coordinating Committee which comes up with a joint effort to resubmit to small groups for their approval.

Initiative 2: Educational Programs Consider Their Program's Issues of Identity

Various factions, such as students, program faculty, program administration, and university/college administrators, meet regularly to consider the program's pluses and challenges (such as dual degrees and employment) and to create a *plan* to focus on and enhance identity among students. (Note: It is essential that university/college administration should be included in this process.)

Some suggestions, which could be instituted immediately, are a student identity journal (begun as students enter program and continued until graduation) and, to enhance involvement, payment of the AATA dues by the program.

In addition, I propose that each master's-level art therapy education program establish a *free group for graduates,* maximum of 10 people, meeting monthly or more, for supervision and nurturing for about two years. Leader is a faculty member or an experienced art therapy clinician.

The final product is a two-page document listing *core values and components of art therapy identity* to be submitted to coordinating group representative.

Initiative 3: Practitioner Art Therapists, Including Private Practice, Consider Their Profession's Identity and Its Challenges

The final product is a two-page document listing core values and components of art therapy identity to be submitted to coordinating group representative.

Initiative 4: Group Composed of Those Who Graduated From Graduate Art Therapy Programs but, Post-Graduate, Have Largely or Entirely Dropped the Art

The discussion here concerns the "whys" of these decisions to "drop out." The final product is a list of these issues, which may be the most important understandings and information for the profession.

Year Two

Initiative 1: By the End of YEAR ONE, All Participants and Groups Will Submit Final Product to the Coordinating Group. Tasks:

- Establish a final document outlining
  1. Core values
  2. Components of Art Therapy Identity
  3. Goals
- Create a **plan** to achieve goals
- Create a **marketing/public relations** plan to present the profession to the community and to the public.

Initiative 2: Carry Out the Marketing/Public Relations Plan

- Delegation of sections of PR plan, as needed.

Initiative 3: Evaluation of Entire Process by Coordinating Group and Other Community Members

Chapter 6

CONCLUSIONS

We are in the second decade of the 21st century, a crucial and essential time for the American art therapy community to come together to reconsider and firmly reestablish issues of professional identity toward a shared public identity. In its history, this complex and innovative profession, strongly grounded in creativity, has made a compelling and largely effective effort toward credibility. That art therapy has been flexible and adaptable has been a good thing. But has it been *too* adaptable and *too* flexible? When do those admirable traits cause problems? The resounding complaint echoed in the essays of this book is that as art therapy has gained in credibility, it has become a profession that many art therapists now consider too rigid, too bureaucratic, and too stifling of the creativity on which it was based. Does the art therapy field need a more singular definition of its identity to clarify itself? To effectively resolve this paradox of a profession achieving credibility without losing its creative edge is—without a doubt—a tremendous challenge. But it can be done and it *must* be done.

This week the fifth edition of the *Diagnostic and Statistical Manual* (*DSM*) by the American Psychiatric Association has been published.[1] Commonly taught in mental health educational programs, the *DSM* is known as the "language" of mental health, mental health facilities, and health insurance. It is also widely and often unfortunately regarded as scientific "truth" by many clinicians and students, rather than as the political document it is. Nevertheless, it has become an extraordinarily important document and an essential part of the mental health world and of our society and culture. The publication of the new *DSM*

---

1. The fourth edition was published in 1994.

213

immediately resulted in a ground swell of criticism because it expands and pathologizes definitions of mental dysfunctions until they cover what many refer to as "normal" life experiences, such as loss.

It has long been eminently clear that the mental health system in the United States is in trouble, money starved, and all but gone. It is commonly noted that we are in an era of increasing gun use and violence, where individual liberties trump community necessities, and the legalities of the mental health system make it all but unusable except after the fact. Medication is ubiquitous. Should we be surprised that zombies are also ubiquitous in popular culture? There is a certain peculiar irony in this expansion of mental dysfunction and pathology in *DSM-5* at this particular time.

Within the art therapy community, ever-expanding complexities of dual identities in licensable educational programs make the development of an art therapy professional identity for the coming generations of art therapists confusing to say the least. There is another central problem: Along with its inherent dualities, the art therapy community struggles with its philosophical worldview that it *is a kind of artist* with additional roots in an aesthetic and empathic perspective. From this, it has been a basic value of the field, evolving from theory, that "interpretation" should be the *client's territory,* and any interpretation the art therapist makes is often mere invention and not based on any "scientific" research or "truth." To date, the field is largely a profession of practitioners, and a practitioner's viewpoint is rightfully cautious, careful, and potential. A good clinician relishes ambiguity and not-knowing and allows for the possibility of possibilities. Considering themselves a form of artists, art therapists think of themselves as individualistic and creative, which makes the paradoxical combination of art with the necessary objectivity of "therapy" as a science a difficult one to sort out to achieve a definable professional identity. Yet it must be done.

To illustrate such complexities combined with the resounding clash of realities, consider the following: The art therapy educators group of the AATA is considering a plan for the future, which would bind together the counseling profession and art therapy education. The AATA denies this and states its goal is art therapy licensing in all 50 states[2] by the end of the decade. Art therapy licensing in all states is neither a

---

2. Currently, five states license art therapists: Kentucky, Maryland, New Mexico, Wisconsin, and New York (as "Creative Arts Therapist").

realistic idea nor one that considers any of the political realities state to state—nor even the huge amount of time and money involved. (Meanwhile, the counseling organization with a large political identity and base continues to push forward.) Additionally, the AATA can no longer claim that it represents a majority of art therapists but only its specific membership, which nationwide is about 5000 people.

If art therapy educators were to adopt any or all of the current draft plan, or become engulfed by a state's adoption of it (such as has already occurred, I understand, in one state), it would have tremendous and serious ramifications for universities, art therapy education, and the profession as a whole. For example, it would define and rigidify who could be hired in college and university programs to teach art therapists. According to the plan, only those from counseling doctoral programs accredited by the counseling (CACREP) professional organization would be acceptable whereas graduates of "other" doctoral programs would not.[3] While it would seem that this thrust is unlikely to happen, in my more than 40 years as an art therapist, I have seen some strange things.

At the beginning of this book, I stated that a major priority for the field is to propel forward and make clear the idea that *art therapy identity is an issue.* I proposed that it is essential that art therapy move forward proactively by carefully defining its identity. I believe that the art therapy community must undertake to explain itself *to itself* and to the mental health world at large in an expansive and meaningful way. How it does this is not merely an important public relations strategy but will have meaning for the lives and careers of many future generations of art therapists and perhaps ensure the profession's survivability. We are at a crossroads, and the time is now. As the Talmud says, If I am not for myself, who will be for me? And being only for myself, what am I? And if not now, when?

---

3. Ohio is already requiring that programs be CACREP-accredited by January 2018.

Appendix A

FIFTEEN DEFINING IDENTITY QUESTIONS

1. How would you describe your personal identity with regard to art therapy? Which elements are most important to you?

2. Does your art therapy identity fit with your employment? Your practice?

3. Do you think art therapy could benefit from a stable, unitary identity? Why or why not?

4. What identity problems are created by the current "umbrella with many definitions model"? Within the art therapy community? Within the mental health community?

   Could you describe an image of the umbrella at this point in art therapy's history (and so on, what values, elements, etc. are contained in/on the umbrella)?

5. There is a notion that doing one's art is necessary for the art therapist. Some believe that an art therapist is another form of artist. Must an art therapist be an artist? Does it matter? Why? What does making art have to do with the personal/professional identity of the art therapist?

6. What would it take for art therapy to move past the duality/ dialectic models of psychology/art, Naumburg/Kramer of the past, which (I believe) imply adversarial right/wrong, into a less competitive model? What would it look like? Do you think this is a good idea for art therapy identity? Is it even possible?

7. Long ago, it was decided that art therapy should be one of the mental health pantheon rather than a rehabilitation or educational therapy such as occupational therapy or recreational/ activity. Then it was thought to be too close to the "medical model" and too "clinified."

   Do you think this defining of art therapy as a mental health discipline should still be the major thrust for art therapy? What are the advantages and disadvantages of it in moving the profession forward toward more credibility?

8. In what way does the AATA contribute to clarity or confusion about art therapy identity? What *should* it do?

9. As a professional membership organization, do you consider the AATA mostly competitive or mostly cooperative?

10. In what way does current art therapy education contribute to or make difficult art therapy identity formation and what *should* it do?

11. Who or what do you think should be responsible for defining art therapy professional identity?

12. How can art therapy be open and "welcoming" to others (e.g., "teach" others how to do it and still portray itself as something special and different)?

13. Does the art therapy profession mostly define itself or does it mostly allow others to define it? What *should* it be?

14. What is the image of art therapy *visible* to the world today?

15. What are your suggestions for the future to help art therapy grow and achieve a more credible identity?

Appendix B

LETTER TO POTENTIAL BOOK PARTICIPANTS

Dear _____,

You are probably aware, I have been interested in issues surrounding the *art therapist's identity* for a long time now–since I got into the biz in 1973 and actively for about the last 15 years. As you may know, Myra Levick and I started an email dialogue on identity a few years back, and many of you contributed.

I have decided to do a book on the subject and have a contract with Charles C Thomas. I will be inviting a short list of participants, and YOU are invited to contribute. (Particulars are below.)

My intention is to attract the brightest minds in the field, and include people with differing opinions and from different "generations." I want to get some new graduates and some "old timers." I may do something of a survey. (I did this with students about the last 5 years before I left Loyola Marymount but never published it.) Along with some chapters on definition, identity formation development of the concept generally and in art therapy and identity's history in art therapy. The meat of the book will be your essays. I know you are a very busy person and probably have written or are writing more than you care to, but I believe this is a unique opportunity to contribute to the art therapy profession in an important way at an important time.

I REALLY WANT YOUR CONTRIBUTION!

I will come up with some defining questions, send them to you, and you can either use or not. If worse comes to worse and writing is a problem for any reason, I will be happy to interview you over the phone, write up the

219

interview, and submit it to you for your additions, corrections, and so on. If individual arrangements need to be made (e.g., for deadlines), I'm happy to try and accommodate you. The essay can be as short as you like, but no longer than 3500 words—about 10 double-spaced pages. Crucial are *honesty and your willingness to express your opinions.* As those of you who know me know, I have no problem with controversy. While there may be some editing of your piece, there won't be any changing or "softening" of your ideas. This is your opportunity to say some of those things you may have been thinking for a long time. For example, do you think the field needs a stable and/or unitary identity at all?

Particulars:
1. By July 15, 2012. Please let me know that you are able to participate by email (mbjunge@whidbey.net).
2. October 15, 2012, is the deadline for submission of your essay.
3. I will be writing the contextual chapters during this time.
4. Editing and telephone interviewing for the next few months.
5. Book submitted to publisher August 2013
6. Published about 6–8 months later in hard, soft cover, and eBooks. You will receive a copy.

(If you want to know who else is participating, I can supply you with a list when this is settled.)

Fondly,
Max
Maxine Borowsky Junge

Some of my ideas:
Art therapy is an interdisciplinary combination of psychology and the arts, and issues of identity and identity formation have been crucial to the development of the profession. They have also been vigorously debated. Many believe that the organized profession began with art psychotherapy but as such was too close to the medical model. In the recent decade or so, art therapy has "gone back to the art," which is now a dominant paradigm often eschewing psychotherapy aspects. Some believe that in its attempts to achieve standards of practice and education, art therapy may have become staid and needs to find a better way to include the creativity for which it is known.

Since the late 1970s, many art therapy education programs have aligned with or integrated another mental health discipline. A primary pragmatic reason for this is that art therapists can graduate with a degree title acceptable to the mental health world and amenable to state licensing requirements. Therefore, they may be able to more easily find employment and practice. (In my opinion, the art therapy profession is likely to remain too small to effectively undertake alone the political struggles that may lead to art therapy state licensing.)

In a dual-degree or integrated program, it is not unusual to be attacked from both sides. For example in the late 1970s when my program at Loyola Marymount University did this because of state licensing regulations, we were accused by many (and publically) in the AATA of "losing the art." (In the Marriage and Family Therapy world, we were accused of trying to "hide" the art.) In reality, the nature or "amount" of art in the program hadn't changed, nor was it being hidden. Recently, as I understand it, the AATA was undertaking a controversial drive to make art therapy a subgroup of Counseling. This thrust is apparently now abandoned, and the AATA is putting its efforts toward working with the Department of Labor to "elevate" art therapy to a master's-level discipline and out of the current category with activity therapists and the like where it currently resides. I believe the AATA does not endorse dual-degree programs.

Identity has been a priority in art therapy, but dual degrees make identity issues more problematic for the art therapist and for the profession. I have seen the following happen: The dual-degreed art therapist, post-master's, is hired for her or his degree title and for something extra–the art. But I believe to do both talk therapy and art therapy is tougher and takes more energy for the clinician. As cases get more difficult and caseloads bigger and overwhelming, the art therapist is liable to give up the art part out of sheer exhaustion and the quite natural wish to be "one of the others" as she or he is often, the only (and lonely) art therapist. I recently had a 1980 art therapy graduate say to me that she thought she was the only one of her cohort still doing art therapy. Perhaps this kind of attrition is normal?

Through their history, art therapists have had to be all things to all people–they are seldom hired with the job title "art therapist" or with much, if any, understanding of what an art therapist is and does. Their master's degree titles may not be art therapy, nor their department titles. As art therapy becomes more known to the general public and to mental health professions, there is a good deal of confusion over what an art therapist is and does and how they may differ from a clinician of another stripe who uses art exercises in therapy or even an artist.

Today, in my opinion, the art therapist in a master's program and in training needs far more direct attention paid to establishing and maintaining an identity. In addition, after graduation, as they work as clinicians, a good deal of support is needed. Perhaps post-graduate institutional support should be mandated. Perhaps the art therapy professional organizations should be involved. What do the fledgling PhD programs contribute to and/or have to say about the issue of identity?

BIBLIOGRAPHY

Allen, P. (1992). Artist in residence. An alternative to "clinification" for art therapists. *Art Therapy, Journal of the American Art Therapy Association, 9,* 22–29.

American Art Therapy Association (2013). Available at http://www.arttherapy.org /aata- aboutus.html.

American Art Therapy Association. (2011, Summer). Business Meeting Minutes (Un-approved).

Anderson, F. (1973, November). *Survey on the use of art therapy in the Midwest.* Paper presented at the American Art Therapy Association conference. Columbus, OH.

Anderson, F., & Landgarten, H. (1974). Survey on the status of art therapy. *American Journal of Art Therapy, 13,* 40–50.

Anderson, F., & Landgarten, H. (1975). Art therapy in the mental health field. *Studies in Art Education, 15,* 45–56. (Revision of Anderson & Landgarten, 1974.)

Ashton-Warner, S. (1963). *Teacher.* London: Secker & Warburg.

Betts, D., & Laloge, L. (2000). Art therapists and research: A survey conducted by the Potomac Art Therapy Association. *Art Therapy, Journal of the American Art Therapy Association, 17*(4), 291–295.

Brennan, C. (2011). The role of research in art therapy master's degree programs. *Art Therapy, Journal of the American Art Therapy Association, 28*(3), 140–144.

Carolan, R. (2001). Models and paradigms of art therapy research. *Art Therapy, Journal of the American Art Therapy Association, 18*(4), 190–206.

Collins, P. (1986). Learning from the outsider within: The sociological significance of Black feminist thought. *Social Problems, 33*(6), 514–532.

Coppock, T. (March 2012). A closer look at developing counselor identity. Knowledge Share, An American Counseling Association Publication. Retrieved June 26, 2012, from http://ct.counseling.org/2012/03/a-closer-look-at-developing -counselor-identity

Deaver, S. (2002). What constitutes art therapy research? *Art Therapy, Journal of the American Art Therapy Association, 19*(1), 23–27.

Elkins, D., Stovall, K., & Malchiodi, C. (2003). American Art Therapy Association, Inc.: 2001–2202 Membership survey report. *Art Therapy, Journal of the American Art Therapy Association, 20,* 28–34.

Erikson, E. (1950). *Childhood and society.* New York: W.W. Norton & Co., Inc.

Erikson, E. (With J. M. Erikson). (1987). *The life cycle completed.* New York: W.W. Norton & Co., Inc.

Faulkner, W. (2011, first published 1950). *Requiem for a nun* (First Vintage international edition). New York: Vintage.

Gantt, L. (1998). A discussion of art therapy as a science. *Art Therapy, Journal of the American Art Therapy Association, 15,* 3–12.

Heller, N. (2012, November 19). Little strangers. *The New Yorker,* pp. 85–90.

Ilger, D. (1990). Credentialing in psychology: A limited need. In L. Bickman & H. Elllis (Eds.), *Preparing psychologists for the 21st century.* Proceedings of the National Conference on Graduate Education in Psychology. Hillsdale, N.J: Earlbaum.

Julliard, E., Gujral, J., Hamil, S., Oswald, E., Smyk, A., & Testa, N. (2000). Art based evaluation in research education. *Art Therapy, Journal of the American Art Therapy Association, 17*(2), 118–124.

Junge, M. (2012a). *Survey of identity in beginning art therapy graduate students.* Unpublished research.

Junge, M. (2012b). *Survey of identity in recently graduated art therapy students.* Unpublished research.

Junge, M. (2008). *Mourning, memory and life itself, essays by an art therapist.* Springfield, IL: Charles C Thomas.

Junge, M. (2010). The modern history of art therapy in the United States. Springfield, IL: Charles C Thomas.

Junge, M., & Linesch, D. (1993). Our own voices: New paradigms for art therapy research. *The Arts in Psychotherapy, 20,* 61–67.

Junge, M., & Maya, V. (1985). Women in their forties: A group portrait and implications for psychotherapy. *Women & Therapy, 4*(3), 3–19.

Junge, M., & Wadeson, H. (2006). *Architects of art therapy, memoirs and life stories.* Springfield, IL: Charles C Thomas.

Kaiser, D., St. John, P., & Ball, B. (2006). Teaching art therapy research: A brief report. *Art Therapy, Journal of the American Art Therapy Association, 23*(4), 196–190.

Kaplan, F. (2000). *Art, science and art therapy: Repainting the picture.* London & Philadelphia: Jessica Kingsley.

Kramer, E. (1958). *Art therapy in a children's community.* Springfield, IL: Charles C Thomas.

Kuhn, T. (1964). *Structure of scientific revolutions.* Chicago, IL: University of Chicago Press.

Landgarten, H. (1976). Changing status of art therapy in Los Angeles. *American Journal of Art Therapy, 15,* 4.

Landgarten, H. (1978). Status of art therapy in Los Angeles. *American Journal of Art Therapy, 5,* 4.

Lear, J. (1998). *Open minded: Working out the logic of the soul.* Cambridge, MA: Harvard University Press.

Linesch, D. (1992). Research in approaches within masters level art therapy training programs. *Art Therapy: Journal of the American Art Therapy Association, 9*(3), 129–134.

Malchiodi, C. (1995). Does a lack of art therapy research hold us back? *Art Therapy, Journal of the American Art Therapy Association, 12,* 261–265.

Malchiodi, C. (2012). *So you want to be an art therapist, part seven: Art therapist identity confusion disorder.* Available at http://www.psychologytoday.com/blog/the-healing-arts/201201/so-you-want-to-be-an-art-therapist/6/24/2012.

Maraniss, D. (2012). *Barak Obama: The story.* New York: Simon and Schuster.

McCall, L. (2005). The complexity of Intersectionality. *Journal of Women in Culture and Society, 30,* 1771–1800.

McElhinney, R. (2008). *Professional identity development: A grounded theory study of child psychology trainees.* Unpublished doctoral dissertation.

McLaughlin, T. (2012, June 12). Drawing together. *Newsletter of the Minnesota Art Therapy Association.*

Moon, C. (2001). *Studio art therapy: Cultivating the artist identity in the art therapist.* London & Philadelphia: Jessica Kingsley.

Naumburg, M. (1966). *Dynamically oriented art therapy: Its principles and practice.* New York: Grune & Stratton. [Reprinted in 1987, Chicago, IL: Magnolia Street.]

Olson, E. (2010, Winter). *Personal identity: The Stanford encyclopedia of philosophy.* Plato, Stanford, edu/entries, identity-personal.

Reynolds, M., Nabors, L., & Quinlan, A. (2000). The effectiveness of art therapy: Does it work? *Art Therapy, Journal of the American Art Therapy Association, 17*(3), 207–213.

Robbins, A. (2006). Moving in and out of the sandbox. In M. Junge & H. Wadeson (Eds.), *Architects of art therapy.* Springfield, IL: Charles C Thomas.

Rodgers, D. (1966). Psychologists as practitioners, not technicians. In H. Dorken & Associates (Eds.), *Professional psychology in transition.* San Francisco: Jossey-Bass.

Rogers, C. (1973). Some new challenges to innovation. *American Psychologist, 28,* 379–387.

Rosal, M. (1998). Research thoughts: Learning from the literature and from experience. *Art Therapy, Journal of the American Art Therapy Association, 15,* 47–50.

Rubin, J. (2001 Second edition). Approaches to art therapy, theory and technique. New York: Brunner-Routledge.

Rubin, J. (2010). *Introduction to art therapy* (2nd ed.). New York: Routledge.

Ryan, A. (2003). *Defining ourselves: I-O psychology's identity quest.* Presidential Address, at the annual conference of the Society for Industrial-Organizational Psychology. Orlando, FL.

Slayton, S., D'Archer, J., & Kaplan, F. (2010). Outcome studies on the efficacy of art therapy: A review of findings. *Art Therapy, Journal of the American Art Therapy Association, 27*(3), 108–118.

Wadeson, H. (2011). *Journaling cancer in words and images: Caught in the clutch of the crab.* Springfield, IL: Charles C Thomas.

Weinrich, P. (1986). The operationism of identity theory in racial and ethnic relations. In J. Rex & D. Mason (Eds.), *Theories of race and ethnic relations.* Cambridge, UK: Cambridge University Press.

ABOUT THE AUTHOR

Maxine Borowsky Junge, PhD, LCSW, ATR-BC, HLM, has been an art therapist for more than 40 years. Since childhood her main passions have been art and how people work. She began formally in the art therapy profession in 1973, teaching in the fledgling clinical art therapy program initiated by Helen Landgarten at Immaculate Heart College, Hollywood, California. She is Professor Emerita at Loyola Marymount University, where she was Chair of the department for many years, and she has also taught at Goddard College and Antioch University-Seattle. Junge has presented her work nationally and internationally.

Dr. Junge received her Bachelor's degree in Painting and Humanities from Scripps College, where, in 2012, she was designated "Distinguished Alumna of the Year." She attended UCLA's graduate program in painting, earned an MSW from USC and completed a PhD from Fielding Graduate University in Human and Organizational Systems. She is a Registered and Board Certified art therapist and received the HLM award from the American Art Therapy Association.

Dr. Junge wrote *A History of Art Therapy in the United States* in 1994 and *The Modern History of Art Therapy* in 2010. These are the only histories in book form of the fascinating and innovative mental health profession of art therapy. She has written six other books, and her favorite is Mourning, Memory, and Life Itself, Essays by an Art Therapist, which contains many of her published essays over the years. Her phenomenological study of visual artists and writers, which resulted in *Creative Realities: The Search for Meanings,* establishes an important alternative theory of creativity.

Dr. Junge's clinical experience includes Cedars-Sinai Hospital–Thalians Community Mental Health Center, Council of Jewish Women, and private practice, all in Los Angeles. In particular, she has always been fascinated by family art therapy. In addition, she has had an organizational development practice.

Twelve years so, she moved to Whidbey Island, north of Seattle, where she continues to supervise, consult, mentor, make art (a series of "Mass Murderers" drawings, most recently), and write. *Identity and Art Therapy* is her seventh book.

227